1/49   8.-

The Tetons

Interpretations of a Mountain Landscape

THE
TETONS

Interpretations of a Mountain Landscape

By FRITIOF FRYXELL

Grand Teton Natural History Association

Moose, Wyoming 1995

Previously published by
University of California Press
Berkeley and Los Angeles
California

Cambridge University Press
London, England

ISBN 0-931895-06-5 HB
ISBN 0-931895-05-7 PB

First printing, 1938
Second printing, 1946
Third printing, 1953
Fourth printing, 1959
Fifth printing, 1966
Sixth printing, 1984
Seventh printing, 1995

Cover photo by Ed Riddell
Lithography by Paragon Press

*To my campfire companions of long ago
—Regina, John, Roald, Redwood, and Grandpa—
this book is lovingly dedicated.*

THE CATHEDRAL GROUP AND JENNY LAKE

"We would that you should stay here a while, to be acquainted with us, and yet more to solace yourselves with the good of these delectable mountains." —*The Pilgrim's Progress*

About Fritiof Fryxell

Interpreter of the Magic Mountains

THIS BOOK IS THE STORY of how the Tetons came to be, and the personal record of a man who loved them.

Fritiof Fryxell's name was powerful once in the high country of the Tetons. When he made his last visit to Grand Teton National Park in 1983—at the age of 83—he received celebrity welcome. In the 1920s and '30s he had climbed all the major mountains in the range, named many of its features, and written about the area with care and love. The power of that love lingers in the very sweep of Grand Teton National Park.

We can still trace his presence here . . . in historic photographs in the Jenny Lake Ranger Station . . . on a wayside exhibit for the Cathedral Group turnout, quoting his description of that formation which he named . . . in the continuing respect of Teton geologists for his scientific work on the mountains . . . in the admiration of modern climbers for his mountaineering feats . . . in the imaginations of those who read this book.

He was a professor, scientist, mountaineer, park ranger, writer, and collector. Yet he used to say that the title he liked best was "interpreter." Each of his varied activities involved acts of interpretation. His deep love of the Tetons centered and inspired all he did.

He was not a native of the region, and until he reached his twenties knew the Tetons only secondhand. He was born

April 27, 1900 in a Midwestern river town, Moline, Illinois, and grew up ranging the woods and limestone bluffs of the area for plants, rocks, and artifacts turned up by plows or washed out by the Mississippi. By the time he was ten he had assembled a museum of these "finds" in his bedroom. His upbringing emphasized the values found in Swedish immigrant homes a century ago: hard work, self-discipline, integrity, and academic achievement, and he never relinquished those values. A father who lacked formal education but spent free time in wide reading encouraged his children's curiosity about the world around them, and expected them to do well in school. All four of them did.

It was from his father that Fryxell first caught the magic of the Tetons. As a small boy he would sit on John Fryxell's lap as the two looked at woodcuts of the west in H.T. Williams' *The Pacific Tourist* (published in 1876), and his father explained each scene in his native Swedish language.

Though images of the Tetons haunted him, it was not until 1924 that Fryxell actually got to see the mountains. By then he had earned degrees in biology and English from Augustana College in Rock Island, Illinois. He would later return to teach and establish a world-famous department of geology. In the mid-twenties, however, he was a graduate student at the University of Chicago, spending a summer, as he put it, "rambling about the West". By train and on foot, from the Black Hills to the Bighorn Mountains to Glacier National Park, through Yellowstone and down the west side of the Tetons, he scouted out a dissertation topic for his doctorate in geology, intoxicated by his freedom. On sight as in art, the Tetons were magic mountains. As subjects of geological study they provided a compact unit, lacking the vast spread of some other ranges. As objects of sheer beauty, they were unmatchable.

So Fryxell joined that long line of trappers, explorers, and homesteaders who made their way through history into Jackson Hole. Even in the late-1920s the trip was still pioneering work as there were no paved roads and the train line ended at Victor, Idaho. Lucky travelers got rides over Teton Pass with an obliging mail truck. After that, long treks through waist-high sagebrush, primitive campsites with intrusive wildlife (the badgers could be especially vicious), and least expensive rations were the rule of field work. The slight (110-pound), tough Fryxell thrived on it.

While he was recording data from the valley, on moraines and outwash plains, he also found himself, like the psalmist, lifting his eyes to the hills, the great Teton peaks to the west. It was only a matter of time until Fryxell went up into the mountains and came down a climbing legend.

At the beginning of his climbing career (1926-1928) he was collecting material for his doctoral thesis on glacial features of Jackson Hole. When his work on the range led to an appointment as the first ranger-naturalist for the newly created Grand Teton National Park (1929-1934), he continued his exploration. He had been asked to establish park educational programs, and to do so he looked for reliable information on the geologic structure and history of the Teton Range. The best records he could find were the dated and generalized Hayden Survey reports of the 1870s. So he launched his own reconnaissance trips. He climbed every major peak, many as first ascents, and traversed most of the canyons in the Tetons.

But scientific curiosity was only part of the appeal. The

spirit of adventure was strong in this wiry, red-headed latter-day Viking with the heroic Norse name ("Fritiof" means "warrior"). The mountains challenged; the rush of danger and conquest exhilarated; the beauty stimulated and calmed.

Most modern climbers find it phenomenal that Fryxell and his sometime partner, fellow ranger Phil D. Smith, ever survived their climbs. The rapidity of the ascents, coupled with the makeshift equipment they used, continues to amaze climbers who follow their routes as Fryxell charted them in *The Teton Peaks and their Ascents*, published in 1932 (the book was revised in 1978 as *Mountaineering in the Tetons— the Pioneer Period*, and edited by Phil Smith). Since the ranger station with its varied duties demanded a 7:00 a.m. to 7:00 p.m. schedule, climbs had to be fitted into twenty-four hour periods on days off. Typically Fryxell would set out around two in the morning, climb trail-less slopes to timberline, scale the peaks, finding new routes, and return by seven the next morning. His equipment consisted of hemp ropes that handled awkwardly and burned the skin, army surplus boots stuffed with extra socks to make them fit his feet, and hobnails put in by the shoemaker in Jackson. Until 1930, when climber Robert Underhill and Kenneth Henderson taught the rangers techniques they had learned in the Alps, Fryxell and Smith climbed without pitons, rapelling, or mechanical assists. Because of their restrictive schedules, they often broke the never-climb-alone rule.

These reconnaissance trips into the mountains yielded a variety of results: campfire talks outside the Jenny Lake Ranger Station, in which Fryxell explained aspects of Teton natural history to Park visitors; gave advice to aspiring climbers, and instigated a system of registration to keep track of them when they climbed. (The system was so successful in reducing accidents and facilitating rescues that it served as a model for other national parks.)

Fryxell's first-hand knowledge of Teton terrain enabled him to give persuasive testimony in the Congressional hearing conducted during the 1940s on whether or not to add a large portion of Jackson Hole to the Park. (Until 1950 Grand Teton National Park was restricted to about 150 miles of the alpine section of the range.) Thanks in part to scientific insights Fryxell presented, Congress voted to enlarge the Park area to its present size. The approximately 700 square mile additions unite the contrasting features of range and valley. At the government's request Fryxell named many features in the range he had come to know so well. The Board of Geographic Names adopted most of his suggestions on June 3, 1931: names like Teewinot, Nez Perce, St. John, Lake Solitude, Bannock Waterfall, Skillet Glacier; Avalanche, Garnet, Cascade, and Indian Paintbrush Canyons, and the famed Cathedral Group described in this book and on the wayside exhibit by the Cathedral Group turnout. In sound and strength of imagery these names interpret both the features and Fryxell's love for them.

The Teton experience served as initiation for the young Fryxell, testing his powers as explorer, scientist, and interpreter. In 1935 he served as geologist for the museum planning staff of the National Park Service in Berkeley, California. He helped plan exhibits for most of the Western national parks and monuments. The exhibit at Devil's Tower National Monument, Wyoming is a sample of their work.

It was at Berkeley that he wrote *The Tetons: Interpretations of a Mountain Landscape*. Diaries, notes, and memories from the Wyoming years, skills developed by his teaching and campfire talks in presenting complex material clearly, and his own reverence for the mountains supplied content and form. Fryxell has been called the last of the nineteenth-century naturalists, even though he lived late into the twentieth century. *The Tetons* justifies this observation. It is spiritual kin to works by John Muir and Francois Matthes, and behind them John Ruskin and the poet William Wordsworth—all of whom Fryxell read and admired and whose grand rhetoric his own style echoes. For him as for them, the processes which science can define bear witness to metaphysical realities: God, intelligent and purposeful, is within the buckling of rock and the rearing of mountains. And beauty is a mystery which holds a great good.

Fryxell loved beauty, loved it as the Romantics did, with an intensity that was hunger. For him as for them, beauty meant an experience located in concrete reality, but linked to and interpenetrating a reality beyond the concrete. In his journal he reveals that for him "a snowstorm or the burning of a candle is a spiritual experience" (January 1933). *The Tetons* is his most direct and complete rendering of this belief. For it was in the mountain landscapes that spiritual realities came to him, clear and vivid, passionately alive.

Science, the senses, and the heart all proclaim the same truth, he asserts in *The Tetons*. Perhaps this explains its enduring appeal.

Clearly the exhilaration of the West defined and energized his abilities. Colleagues have noted the unusual breadth of his geological work, encompassing the fields of geomorphology, glacial geology, structural geology, seismology, and metamorphic petrology. About two-thirds of this research

About Fritiof Fryxell

concerns the Teton-Jackson Hole area. Yet despite—or rather because of—this focal point for energy, much of his important work went on in other venues.

One was Rock Island. In 1929 he had returned to Augustana College to establish the department of geology. This was a bold venture. It occurred amid the national furor that followed the 1925 Scopes trial challenging the teaching of evolution, a time when other church-related colleges— Augustana is affiliated with the Lutheran Church—were shying away from earth science. Backed by a sympathetic administration, Fryxell dealt with intellectual risk as he had met the physical challenges of mountain-climbing. Under his direction the department came to exert influence in the geologic community disproportionate to its size. Most professional geologists have heard of Augustana, not surprisingly, since many of them were students of Fryxell or his successors. These students have risen to the top in all facets of geologic activity, industrial, governmental, and academic. Some have followed his path West to study mountains. Fryxell was instrumental also in founding the organization that has become the National Association of Geology Teachers, and he was the first recipient of its Neil Miner Award for excellence in the teaching of geology. At Augustana, both a museum and an endowed professorship carry his name, and his students—several of whom have taught in the department—carry his spirit.

Fryxell's other significant arena of activity was Washington, D.C. , where in 1942 he began one of the most crucial enterprises of his career. He joined the Military Geology Unit, an organization the Saturday Evening Post termed "one of the most interesting and important additions

to the collective brain of the United States Army . . . 100 of
the ablest geologists . . . this country could mobilize." In a
subterranean warren of offices in the nation's capital, they
devoted their professional expertise to solving problems
which combat troops would encounter half a world away—
problems of how to plan and execute military operations in
remote, often little-known areas. Their work was top-secret;
their hours grueling. Often they worked far into the night
scrutinizing aerial photographs and geologic and topographic maps; studying surveys and reports (most in languages
other than English); making deductions about terrain, water
resources, and landing sites; translating those deductions
into nontechnical language, and getting the reports printed,
bound, and flown to actual battle sites—all within deadlines
so tight that the staff averaged sixty- to eighty-hour work
weeks and round-the-clock production was not unusual.
Fryxell, soon promoted to assistant chief of the unit, never
missed a deadline, produced meticulously accurate reports,
and yet according to colleagues seemed never to hurry. He
did similar work with British counterparts, and in 1945 was
assigned to Manila as chief of the terrain research team at
General MacArthur's headquarters. Here the staff focused
their efforts on the Pacific Theater. They had even prepared
reports for a planned invasion of Japan.

But Fryxell could not leave the West for long, and the West
never left him. Back in 1935 he had noted in his journal that
he was "trying to preserve my patience and forget my long-
ing to be in the West by devoting part of each day to writing." (As a matter of fact, the "writing" project was a draft
of this book.) And so when the war ended, and he had
helped set in motion reconstruction efforts in the

About Fritiof Fryxell

Philippines, he returned to Western projects and studies. He initiated a cooperative research agreement between the National Park Service and the U.S. Geological Survey in 1945. Then he devoted seventeen years to finishing the work of geologist Francois E. Matthes, a mentor and friend, who died in 1948 leaving behind field notes and diaries for projected publications on the Sierra Nevada. The result of Fryxell's reconstructive writing and editing was four magnificent interpretive volumes and a U. S. Geological Survey Professional Paper on the glacial geology of Sequoia National Park.

His feeling for the Tetons linked him with those who shared that feeling. A student of geologic history, he wrote biographies of Western geologists for Encyclopedia Britannica and assembled a large collection of materials on F.V. Hayden, the first surveyor of the Teton Range. He formed lasting friendships with some of the remaining pioneers of the Jackson Hole area, and, in various western history periodicals, wrote their stories. And because his spiritual as well as his scientific energies were engaged by the Western experience, he found himself drawn to Western artists, many of whom he befriended and sponsored. He assisted Ruth Moran, daughter of Thomas Moran (1837-1926), in inventorying and cataloguing her father's watercolors, drawings, and papers, and wrote the first biography of the nineteenth-century artist, *Thomas Moran: Explorer in Search of Beauty* (1958). He encouraged the creative activity of pioneer Teton photographer William Henry Jackson (1853-1942) well into Jackson's nineties. He arranged for Augustana College to sponsor exhibits by Birger Sandzen (1871-1954) and Olaf Moller (1903-?), and he collected their works by purchase and by gift. In 1991 the Augustana College Art Gallery mounted an exhibit of western art from the Fryxell collection. Fryxell's work as a collector, showcased in this exhibit, earned him posthumous honors in the Illinois Academy of Fine Arts' annual Awards program.

While his professional life brought almost uninterrupted satisfaction, his personal life was both bright and dark. He enjoyed a strong marriage: his wife Regina Holmen Fryxell, a gifted Augustana classmate, reaffirmed the values instilled in his family home. She shared a Scandinavian-American background of discipline, dedication to work, and uncompromising integrity. Mrs. Fryxell was a musician and composer whose anthems and liturgical settings earned her national recognition. The energy she gave to her work matched his own; her love for music encouraged his musical interests (he sang with local church choirs and small ensembles), and refined his taste. If her ardor for outdoor living didn't quite equal his, her spirit and skill did. In the summer of 1938 the Fryxells packed up their three children, all under ten and the youngest a baby of seven months, plus Fryxell's eighty-four-year-old father. They set out for Wyoming, where they lived for a month in a large tepee just south of the Jenny Lake Ranger Station. While Fryxell and his colleagues scouted the area in all-day geological field work, Mrs. Fryxell cared for the family's needs, cooking and washing over the fire in the center of the tepee. Many years later she was asked whether she found it hard work doing domestic tasks under such primitive conditions. She smiled quietly. "Not too much work." The response was characteristic. Throughout her life she respected Fryxell's professional commitments and his impassioned need for excellence, and allowed him space for both.

But there was also tragedy. Two of his three brilliant sons died in car accidents, John in 1953 while pursuing graduate studies in political science at the University of Illinois, and Roald, a professor of anthropology at Washington State University, Pullman, while returning from a field trip in 1974. Dr. Roald Fryxell's anthropological and geological work commanded international attention. In Washington state in 1968, he discovered the ten thousand year-old Marmes Man, the oldest human remains in the Western hemisphere. In 1969, he designed the apparatus used by the Apollo XI astronauts for collecting core samples of the moon's surface—and then served on the team of ten scientists who analyzed the lunar rock and soil brought back. John was twenty-three years old and a promising scholar when he died; Roald was forty, married, with two teenaged children, a scientist who had achieved largely and planned much more.

In 1983, three years before he died, Fryxell made his last trip to the Tetons. By then the achievements and the tragedies of his life were completed acts. The deaths of his sons remained sources of shock and pain he was still wrestling. I believe he came finally to peace with these losses, and this last trip to the Tetons helped the healing.

I knew Dr. Fryxell during his last years. I have him in memory now in many pictures. The clearest is here, in the high country of the Tetons, on that last trip. At eighty-three he is a tiny elf with a big shock of untidy hair and a wide smile, standing against the vivid mountains he once climbed in shoes so worn they slid against the rocks. As the power of the mountains touched him, the power of his response reaches us in this book. And I think if love gives energy and energy distills essence, then somewhere in these peaks Fryxell is climbing.

An unpublished verse he wrote July 5, 1930, after completing the first ascent of Nez Perce, expresses his sense of transcendent power. Together we finished the final version in 1985.

Morning and mountains;
The tall peaks stand
With their faces raised
Like a pilgrim band.
Each is dressed,
Ascetic, in white,
And shines with a single
And purified light.

Yet about us the lakes
And dim forests dream on,
Reluctant to stir,
Though the darkness is gone:
And of all the earth's hosts
Only we are abroad
In this hour when the peaks
Are communing with God.

ANN BOADEN
Augustana College
March 1995

NOTE: This introduction draws from personal interviews and conversations with Dr. Fritiof Fryxell.

About the Book

I FEEL THAT THE READER of this booklet should have, in order to enhance his or her appreciation of it, a little background information on its remarkable author. I have in front of me as I write, a battered, much worn 129-page rare classic, a 1930 publication: *Glacial features of Jackson Hole, Wyoming* by F.M. Fryxell. This was his Ph.D. dissertation and it has been the basis for all subsequent geologic-geomorphic work in the Teton-Jackson Hole region. Alongside this publication is the later booklet *The Tetons—Interpretations of a Mountain Landscape*, the subject of this foreword. Both publications are written so simply, clearly and without jargon or ambiguity that I have long used them as examples, for students, of the finest kind of scientific writing. They served as models for our own booklet *Creation of the Teton Landscape* which was dedicated to "Fritiof M. Fryxell, geologist, teacher, writer, mountaineer, and the first ranger-naturalist in Grand Teton National Park. All who love and strive to understand the Teton Landscape follow in his footsteps."

For 45 years, Dr. Fryxell was on the geology faculty of Augustana College. The standards of excellence that he set were transmitted to several thousand undergraduates, more than 150 master's students and more than 60 doctoral students in geology. Among these, Dr. Leland Horberg and Dr. Rudolph Edmund produced classic studies of their own on the Teton region. Dr. Fryxell was one of the founders of the National Association of Geology Teachers. He was awarded two honorary degrees in recognition of his scholarly achievements. His melding of science, philosophy, and teaching have likewise been carried on through successive generations in his own family. His son, the late Professor Roald Fryxell, distinguished geologist and anthropologist in his own right, "one of the Nation's most important scientific figures," is recognized, not only for his many professional publications and awards, but also for a short philosophical gem titled: *The interdisciplinary dilemma–a case for flexibility in academic thought* (1977). In 1984, Roald Fryxell's daughter, Jenny, in collaboration with the late Dr. Donald L. Smith, contributed to a geological memoir a significant and well-written paper titled: *Paleotectonic implications of arkose beds in Park Shale (Middle Cambrian), Bridger Range, south-central Montana.*

A little-known but major contribution by Dr. Fryxell to the welfare of the United States was the application of his geological talent and his sense of the importance of landscape terrain to military geology, 1941-45. Responsibility was, in part, his for evaluating shore-landing sites and battlegrounds in the South Pacific, Europe and Africa, each on a crash, day-to-day, top-secret basis. There were endless deadlines, frantic searches for worldwide geologic literature on far-away places, and written in many languages, directing scores of translators, and above all, knowing that thousands of lives as well as the success of many military campaigns depended on his judgement.

Dr. Fryxell's interest in mountaineering and history, both local and regional, was encouraged by his experiences in

About the Book

the Tetons. *Mountaineering in the Tetons—the pioneer period 1898-1940* was one product of this interest. A second was an elegant and appreciative book about another great interpreter of landscapes, *Francois Matthes and the marks of time—Yosemite and the High Sierra*. For many years Dr. Fryxell collected the most complete assemblage of documents and memorabilia (now at the American Heritage Center University, Laramie, Wyoming) on Dr. F.V. Hayden, the famous pioneer geologist who made the initial geological exploration of the Teton – Jackson Hole – Yellowstone Park region in the 1870s. Related biographical research was done on the famous photographer, W.H. Jackson, and the artist, Thomas Moran, both of whom were nationally known for their works that depicted the glories of the Jackson Hole-Teton-Yellowstone region.

The Tetons—Interpretations of a Mountain Landscape exemplifies the most effective utilization of the multiple talents of a great but humble man whose goal in writing it was to disseminate in an exciting way, scientific knowledge, appreciation of the unique landscape, and his own philosophy of the natural world. As a result of his wisdom and eloquence, the readers of this booklet will become more aware of the richness and challenges of the dynamic Teton region.

J. DAVID LOVE
U.S. Geological Survey
May 8, 1984

Contents

The Rugged Teton Country

WHEN IT WAS MADE a state in 1890, Wyoming was allowed to retain its old territorial name, which originated in an Indian word meaning the "large plains." The name is as appropriate as it is beautiful, for nowhere are the Great Plains more truly great than in Wyoming. Here they spread out toward the far horizon in undulating swells and tablelands that follow each other in seemingly endless succession, in an expanse as vast and limitless as that of the ocean. Treeless, they offer no obstruction to a view of the splendid vault of heaven, where pass daylong processions of stately clouds, and where, at night, burn the stars with a brilliance and in a profusion rarely known in lower elevations and more humid climates. How spacious these landscapes are! Their bigness brings a sense of spiritual exaltation, to which is added the sheerly physical exhilaration felt when in a rarefied atmosphere. Lying a mile and a half above the sea, the Wyoming plains are actually high plateaus. Here lungs seem to double in capacity; yet though he breathe ever so deeply of this sparkling air, the traveler can never inhale enough.

Wyoming is likewise a state of noble mountain ranges. To mention only the more impressive, there are the Medicine Bow, the Bighorn, the Wind River, the Absaroka, and the Teton ranges. To one who has been among them their names will call out of the past a flood of unforgettable im-

1]

pressions: the fragrance of sage or pine after rain, the glow-
ing sunsets with which the days close and that night after
night outline the long broken skyline, or a recurrence of
that sense of profound solitude that comes to one when in
regions as uncrowded as these. Gradually the Wyoming
ranges are becoming familiar to our people, at least by
name, but in a highstrung and ofttimes feverish social order
like ours, so much in need of the unhurried composure that
may be gained from intimate living with mountains, they
should be better known.

Throughout eastern and central Wyoming the ranges are
independent features, each more or less completely isolated.
Thus the Laramie, Medicine Bow, Bighorn, and Wind River
ranges reach far into the plains and divide them into broad
basins. In this meeting, mountains and plains each enhance
the splendor of the other; and grandly simple are the lines
of the landscapes that with the clouds they compose.

The Continental Divide in its adventurous course through
North America traverses Wyoming from southeast to northwest. Like an ardent mountaineer it is devoted to the high
places, keeping to the most rugged of the ranges and descending to lowlands only to attain mountains that beckon
from beyond. It enters from Colorado by the Sierra Madre,
but where this terminates in the Red Desert the divide, like
the overland travelers who also came this way, finds the
course troublesome to follow. Once across these streamless
wastes it mounts to the Wind River crest, and for a hundred
miles or more heads exultantly down a line of resplendent
snowy peaks. In northwestern Wyoming, amidst the sources
of three great divergent river systems—the Colorado, the
Columbia, the Missouri—the watersheds once more grow

indistinct, and here, like many another mountaineer forced to make shift as woodsman, the Continental Divide comes down from the mountains and wanders doubtfully through the forested plateaus and so, at last, out of the state.

In this region, where Wyoming's otherwise simple geographical pattern breaks into a complex massing of mountains and plateaus, there lies the volcanic and hydrothermal area which has become world celebrated by reason of its geysers and hot springs. The Yellowstone wonderland—who has not heard of it? Around it the Wyoming mountains have crowded close, as if the better to guard it, raising barriers to exploration so effective that not until within the memory of men still living were the mysteries of its wilderness fully disclosed.

Yet Yellowstone National Park is primarily a region of volcanic plateaus, and it is not here that the grandeur of the Rocky Mountains finds highest expression. For this, a Yellowstone traveler must look to the south, and if on a clear day he visits the summit of Mount Washburn or crosses any one of several high places on the plateau, as at Shoshone Point, he may have pointed out to him, so distant as to be near the limits of visibility, an isolated group of mountain peaks—the Tetons. There is magic in the name, and contagion. Weary tourists, surfeited with much-seeing, catch the eagerness of their fellows who gaze across the timbered expanses until, beyond, they distinguish for themselves the distant summits. There is no mistaking them. Fifty, perhaps nearly one hundred miles away, the Tetons appear less substantial than the clouds poised above them, and their blueness is that of water colors, in quality like the blue of the sky they pierce, but slightly deeper. How sharp the slender spires! Points so delicate and ethereal seem to have nothing in common with the ordinary, solid substances of earth, yet one must believe, against the evidence of the senses, that in nearer views these mountain peaks will prove to be rock-ribbed like others.

To see the Tetons, however, at closer range was, until recently, impractical for most travelers; and so decade after decade Yellowstone visitors by the hundreds of thousands paused for fleeting glimpses of the peaks, all that their crowded schedules could allow, and were whisked on. But back into the world of men and machines they must have carried with them the recollection of a vision ineffably fine and uplifting.

It was truly a promised land which these travelers of an earlier generation beheld. Very early in the development of our country's system of national parks it was urged that the Tetons should be assigned national parkhood, inevitably so. Between this proposal, urged as long ago as the 'nineties by pioneer conservationists like C. D. Walcott, and the enactment of the federal legislation that made it a reality lay many obstacles, and these were not all hurdled until nearly four decades had passed; but on February 26, 1929, as one of the final achievements of his administration, Calvin Coolidge signed the act that added to our federal recreational areas this superb alpine region through establishment of Grand Teton National Park.

No longer are the Tetons unattainable. From the east, west, north, and south, modern highways reach to their feet, where all highways must end, since to insure that the range remain as nearly as possible in its original state of wild grandeur the framers of the park law wisely stipulated that within the park boundaries no construction of roads or hotels should be permitted.

Now each summer over these approaches journey tens of thousands of visitors. The majority do not linger long in the park nor wander far from the highways, but find rest and contentment for a few days along the tranquil lakes, or forgetfulness of self and whatever of worry may have followed them hither as they watch the ceaseless play of clouds and shadows among the peaks. Yet each year a larger number grow aware that only from trails can one come to know mountains intimately, and to these the highways are simply places of departure.

The trails lead far up the canyons, past the peaks, and into the high back country, where await scenes and adventures scarcely suggested by what can be viewed from below, a region not at all reserved for the relatively few who are skilled in mountain craft but freely open to anyone young or old in possession of ordinary good health and judgment, where indeed life and limb are likely to be far safer than on the thoroughfares of a modern city.

Tens of thousands of visitors each summer! And inevitably the numbers will increase; perhaps it is only a matter of time until the main stream of Yellowstone travel will flow north and south past the Tetons. Here many will pause in tribute to the high peaks, and in so doing taste afresh of the wholesomeness of outdoor life; or through viewing scenes like these be moved to new depths of wonder and reverence. Here the visitor may come to know the enduring satisfactions that derive from a philosophy of protection rather than of exploitation, that come to him who has learned to live abundantly while he lets live, and that are his who ap-

preciates Nature's beauty the better because he views it
understandingly, reading in its own records from its own
characters what it has to say about itself.

These are the wholesome lessons that our people are
learning in the national parks everywhere, from Alaska to
Arizona and from Hawaii to Maine. In an age grown cal-
lous and sophisticated, a return to the clean out-of-doors,
God's forest and mountain temples, can be productive only
of unqualified good, perhaps in a measure far beyond
anything we now dare dream.

MOUNT MORAN FROM THE SNAKE RIVER

Photos, Ed Riddell

THE GRAND TETON FROM THE SNAKE RIVER

Photo, Ed Riddell

THE TETON RANGE FROM THE SHADOW MOUNTAIN ROAD

Photo, Jim Olson

THE VALLEY FLOOR FROM MOUNT TEEWINOT

The Mountains and Valley

THE MOST RUGGED and distinctive portion of the Teton Range is included in the 150 square miles of Grand Teton National Park. On the map this park appears as a long, narrow tract adjacent to the Idaho-Wyoming line. It is nine miles in maximum width and extends north and south through a distance of twenty-seven miles. Its northern extremity lies within a dozen miles of the oldest and most famous of all national parks, Yellowstone. Geographically, Grand Teton National Park may be defined briefly by the statement that it embraces the area lying between the watershed and the east base of the Teton Range, coinciding, therefore, with the Teton east slope.

The Tetons cannot be considered apart from the beautiful valley bearing the strange name of "Jackson Hole" which adjoins them on the east and provides them with a setting so nearly perfect. Encompassed round about by impressive highlands—the Yellowstone plateaus on the north, the Gros Ventre Mountains on the east, and the Tetons on the west— this valley is one of the most sequestered and severely isolated in the entire Rocky Mountain region. It was named in 1829 by Captain William Sublette, noted fur trapper of the period, after his partner, David E. Jackson, who had shown a liking for the valley that we can readily understand. The term "hole" was used by early trappers in much the sense of "basin," and was applied to any mountain-girt valley.

7]

Jackson Hole lies near the crest of the Pacific slope, the Continental Divide passing to the northeast only twenty miles distant, thus missing the Tetons entirely. Unlike most valleys of its type, which are much interrupted by ridges and badlands, Jackson Hole has a floor of singular flatness—a wide, cobble-strewn plain, for the most part given over to sagebrush, that slopes evenly southward from an altitude of 7,000 feet at the one extremity to a thousand feet less at the other, with an area exceeding 400 square miles. The master stream of all the contiguous country is the Snake River—its name descriptive of its course but probably given with reference to the Snake or Shoshoni Indians, through whose country it flows—and Jackson Hole occupies the central portion of its headwaters area. Mountain tributaries with sources in the snow fields of the bordering ranges converge into it, the Snake River receiving these one by one as it traverses the length of the valley. Entrenched in the terraced plain, it follows a braided course that is defined by marginal groves of aspen, spruce, and fine old cottonwoods.

Toward this, the Jackson Hole side, the Teton Range presents a front of extraordinary steepness, one of the most precipitous and spectacular to be found on the continent, if not in the world. Except for Teton Pass (altitude, 8,431 feet) and a few other low places at its southern end, the range is for all practical purposes an insuperable barrier. Over forty miles in length, it springs abruptly from the valley and, but a few miles west of its base, attains elevations of from 9,000 to nearly 14,000 feet above the sea. Thus most of the range is lifted above the forests into realms of bare rock and perpetual snow, and in its deeper recesses glaciers still linger. The beetling gray crags, sheer precipices, and perennial snow fields as seen from this side are greatly enhanced in grandeur by the complete absence of foothills and by contrast with the flat floor of Jackson Hole from which they are viewed.

It is this view that has made the Tetons celebrated; however, as seen from the west, across Teton Basin, Idaho, they are scarcely less splendid, though in setting very different because of the foothills and forested plateaus that intervene. From Tetonia, adjacent to the foothills, or from Ashton, twenty-five miles west, the views are especially fine. At these points one looks up at the Tetons from elevations from 500 to 2,000 feet lower than the level of Jackson Hole, so that the peaks tower correspondingly higher. Teton Basin itself, the "Pierre's Hole" of the early West (declared by Jim Bridger to be "the finest valley in the world"), is now dotted with farms. In harvest time its grainfields sweep up to the Teton foothills in an unbroken golden carpet wholly unlike the silvery gray plains on the Jackson Hole side, but no less beautiful.

In rich measure the Teton Range exhibits all the scenic features which result from an intense glacial experience. Here the beauty that lies in wooded lakes and alpine tarns, no less than the majesty of profound canyons, finds glorious expression. Yet probably none will contest the statement that the superlative feature of the range is its display of peaks. If any assert that they have been disappointed in mountains elsewhere, let them view these; it is difficult to believe that anyone could turn away from the Tetons with expectations unfulfilled, however highly pitched.

Standing in single or broken rank along the full length of the range, the peaks that comprise the Tetons make an array that is truly notable. At least a dozen are so bold in outline and prominent in position as to arrest attention. In order of descending altitude, those with names are the Grand Teton (13,766 feet), Mount Owen (12,922), Middle Teton (12,798), Mount Moran (12,594), South Teton (12,-505), Mount Teewinot (12,317), Buck Mountain (11,923), Nez Perce (11,900), Mount Wister (11,480), Mount St. John (11,412), and Bivouac Peak (11,045). Of the peaks that are less prominent, many of them simply because they stand back from the mountain front, there are even more that deserve acquaintance: Cloudveil Dome (12,026), Teepe Pillar (11,616), Eagles Rest (11,257), Table Mountain (11,-101), Prospectors Mountain (11,231), Rockchuck Peak (11,150), Rolling Thunder (10,902), Mount Hunt (10,-775), Symmetry Spire (10,546), Storm Point (10,040), and many others. It is impossible to count the host of prominent pinnacles and crags, most of them nameless, which likewise add to the amazing jaggedness of the Teton skyline.

As the point from which they are viewed is shifted, the summits change greatly in profile and relative position, but one who studies them attentively will quickly learn to recognize each regardless of the side from which it is seen.

The Grand, Middle, and South Tetons are the historic *Trois Tetons* (meaning the "three breasts") of the early French *voyageurs*. It is this trio, seen to the best advantage only from the west and southwest, that more than a century ago made the Tetons noted as landmarks to the roving trappers, who, guiding their courses by the three easily distinguished summits, crossed Teton Pass on their seasonal migrations to and from their remote trapping grounds.

Following the range inward from either end, one discovers that it rises higher and higher and, with respect to the majesty of its canyons and peaks, becomes ever more magnificent. A climax is attained southwest of Jenny Lake in an extraordinary group of gigantic summits whose dominating figure is the Grand Teton, the peak after which the park takes name. Here, in the four-mile-long area between Avalanche and Cascade canyons, stand six of the loftiest and most distinguished mountains of the range: the South, Middle, and Grand Tetons, Mount Owen, Teewinot, and Nez Perce, together with Cloudveil Dome and the many spires which surround the great summits. The massing of these striking features within such small compass calls to mind Yosemite Valley; among our mountains it has no parallel.

These peaks have been called the "Cathedral Group," especially as viewed from the northeast. Scarcely an original comparison, yet to what else may the group be likened? In its contemplation, or in seeking to convey to others some suggestion of its sublimity, one's mind inevitably returns again and again to this figure of speech.

More evident here than in many of the great cathedrals of men is the Gothic note. It is seen in the profiles of the countless firs and spruces congregated like worshippers on the lower slopes; it reappears higher in the converging lines of spire rising beyond spire; it attains supreme expression in the figures of the peaks themselves that, towering above all else, with pointed summits direct one's vision and thoughts yet higher.

Cathedral-like indeed is this scene in late afternoon once the sun has retired behind the range, when great parallel shafts of light pass between the peaks slantingly across the valley floor; or when, a few hours later during the fleeting

moments in which sky and mountains are together trans-
figured, the natural hues of the summits change swiftly,
marvelously, into delicate shades of rose and blue and lavender, as if colored by light from stained-glass windows.

Like organs playing in side chapels are the waterfalls
within the canyons, each of tone and volume befitting its
own sanctuary, yet scarcely audible when one steps out into
the high vaulted chancel. But when in storm is added the
vibrant and full-throated chorus of the wind as it issues
from the canyons, sounding through the forests and lash-
ing the lakes into waves that beat upon the shores—then
every hall and recess of the Teton Cathedral is filled with
solemn, resounding music.

A cathedral, yes! One that in proportions and vastness
is as far beyond comprehension as in grandeur it is beyond
adequate description; a mountain temple, whose clustered,
tapering spires, soaring aloft to heights a mile or more overhead, are ofttimes lost in driving mists, and when disclosed
are seen to carry never-melting fields of snow.

Irrespective of hour or season, whether viewed on clear
days or stormy, the Tetons are so surpassingly beautiful
that one is likely to gaze silently upon them, conscious of
the futility of speech. Besides providing that inspiration
whose source is in the sublime, the Tetons have been to
many an intellectual stimulus, kindling interest in the ways
of mountain building, leading perhaps to other ventures
into the unlimited fields of earth study.

True appreciation of landscape comes only when one is
alive to both its beauty and its meaning. It is encouraging
to observe the increasing awareness of this fact on the part
of present-day travelers to the national parks.

The Building of a Range

THE TETON RANGE is exceptional for the simplicity and grandeur of its major geologic features. These record the manner of its origin, and the stages through which it has passed.

As he views the range, a thoughtful observer must remark the absence of foothills along its east base, and he is likely to be impressed above all else by the suddenness with which the mountain front rises from the flat valley to snow-clad summits towering six or seven thousand feet above it. How did it come about, he asks, that these peaks were upthrust in forms of such astounding height and sharpness?

The Teton peaks as such were not individually upthrust. They attained their eminence and form through being carved from a common mass which was originally somewhat plateau-like in character—just as, under the hand of a sculptor, figures are chiseled from a block of stone. In fact, the Teton Range is rightly thought of in this way, as a piece of sculpturing, colossal in scale and superb in composition.

As geologists classify mountains, this range is one of the most impressive known examples of the "fault-block" type; that is, it was formed when a block of the earth's outer rocks was fractured ("faulted"), uplifted, and tilted. If long ago in human terms, this event was nevertheless almost recent as the geologist must view the flight of time, and therefore the Teton Range is to be considered as geologically still very young. Since its uplift the block has undergone ceaseless sculpturing by streams, glaciers, and other natural agencies, which have carved it into its present rugged aspect. The attack of these agencies continues, and must inevitably at last reduce the now imposing mountains to a landscape of low, subdued relief.

A geological interpretation of the Tetons may logically begin, therefore, with a consideration of the block from which they were chiseled, and this takes us back some three-score million years[1] to the time of the building of the Rocky Mountains, that is, to the end of the interval in earth history known as the Cretaceous period.

Stresses which had long been accumulating in the outer portion of the earth (even today science understands but little of the nature and source of such mountain-building agencies) had increased to the point where they finally exceeded the strength of the rocks and forced them to yield, with the result that throughout a vast belt extending at least from Alaska to Cape Horn, one-third of the circumference of the globe, the surface strata and deep-lying rocks on which they rest were fractured, folded, uplifted, and otherwise greatly deformed. In this manner the Rockies and their southward continuation, the Andes, came into existence, not as a single cataclysmic upthrust, but through a long series of complexly interrelated earth movements. As one episode late in this stupendous sequence of events, which occurred in the middle or later part of the Tertiary, the geologic period that succeeded the Cretaceous, the Teton Range was formed in northwestern Wyoming.

[1] This time figure and those in later pages are taken from the 1936 report of the Committee on the Measurement of Geologic Time, National Research Council, Washington, D. C.

Photo, Ed Riddell

A GLIMPSE OF THE TETONS

GLACIER CARVED U-SHAPED CANYON AND THE GRAND TETON

In this region the earth was broken along a north–south fracture, geologically termed a "fault" because the section west of it was uplifted relative to that east of it. The uplift was greatest next to the fracture, where it involved a displacement exceeding 7,000 feet, and decreased toward the west, so that the block was given a pronounced westward tilt. The uplifted area, which was over forty miles long and about one-third as wide, must therefore be visualized as strongly unsymmetrical in cross section, with its crest close to the east margin, its exposed edge a steep and narrow east slope, its tilted top a much broader slope descending gently to the west.

Despite all subsequent modifications, the Teton Range still exhibits many characteristics which clearly bespeak its origin as a fault block. The remarkable straightness of the east front of the range, the "hanging" position of the east-slope canyon, the termination of the intercanyon ridges in triangular facets—these features all find their explanation in the fact that the east slope resulted from faulting. There are no foothills along the east base of the mountains because here the rocks are cleanly cut off along the Teton fault; but along the west base, where the rocks are upturned instead of fractured, foothills do occur.

There is marked structural similarity between the Teton Range and the Sierra Nevada of California, for both are fault blocks whose westward tilt gives them contrasting slopes. In the comparison, however, one must recall their difference in size. The Tetons occupy an area only one-tenth as long and one-fifth as wide as the Sierra Nevada, yet they have a relief of the same order of magnitude. Scenically the two show other points of contrast. The usual approach to the Sierra Nevada is from the west, and in ascending it by the great western canyons the traveler passes through a succession of zones each of heightened grandeur till he attains the snowy crest of the High Sierra itself. Quite different is the introduction to the Tetons. The first glimpse is usually from the east, and the three possible approaches—Lewis River, Hoback Canyon, and Togwotee Pass—offer little preparation for the mountain panorama with which the traveler finds himself face to face as he enters the open stretches of Jackson Hole.

It is certain that the uplift of the Teton block was not accomplished by one cataclysm but rather by many small faulting movements distributed over a long period. And as geologic investigation has been extended into the mountains, it has been found that the block itself is internally complicated by a number of lesser faults with displacements of some hundreds of feet paralleling the long axis of the block or crossing it in various directions. Such fracturing might be expected in view of the differential stresses involved in uplifting a mass so large, and the likelihood that following the major uplift here and there local settling would take place.

There is evidence to indicate that an important fault or succession of faults extends along the west base of the high peaks, from the vicinity of Buck Mountain northward approximately parallel to the main Teton fault. In the saddle west of Buck Mountain the sedimentary beds are sharply upflexed along the line of faulting. The great alpine peaks would thus appear to have been carved from a narrow wedge that, along the east margin of the uplifted tract, was upthrust above the rest of the block. The superior height of the peaks in relation to adjacent portions of the range finds explanation in this interpretation, as perhaps does also the straight alignment of the Three Tetons and Mount Owen.

Throughout the Teton block, as it began to rise, stream courses were established, and with continued elevation these tended to become straight, parallel channels extending from the crest eastward and westward down the slopes. But stream tributaries, like deft, sensitive fingers, are ever searching out areas of soft or fractured rock: thus among the Teton streams some, such as Phillips and Open creeks, discovered shattered rock zones due to secondary faults, and along them, as well as along other lines of weakness, developed their channels. Probably there are a number of faults on the Teton east slope of which no evidence exists today except the canyons that mark their courses.

With continued uplift came a stage when the passing air currents, in surmounting the block, were compelled to rise so high that their moisture condensed. Precipitation over the elevated region was thereby increased. The streams, ever gaining in volume and velocity, now flowed along with the fine enthusiasm and vigor of youth, and like a group of skilled artisans singing at work went about their business of sculpturing the range. The initial valleys were deepened into canyons, and the latter, at their heads, notched the crest of the block, shaping it into cols and peaks. If out of the past we could call forth the range as it appeared at this early time, perhaps in it we could recognize many features ancestral to the present peaks, passes, and canyons.

It will be recalled that because of its tilt the Teton block was unsymmetrical in cross section. As a consequence, so far as ability to cut canyons was concerned, the short east-flowing streams had, by virtue of steeper courses, a tremendous advantage over the longer west-flowing streams. Therefore they not only cut deeper canyons but they persistently extended their sources westward and by so doing inexorably encroached upon the west slope, diverting its drainage down their own channels. As a result, the watershed was steadily shifted westward, and the narrow east slope was widened at the expense of the west.

This migration of the watershed down the west slope is still in progress, and, although the difference between the two slopes remains striking, definite progress has been made toward equalization of the two—the ultimate goal. In most places the watershed is several miles west of where it once was and, as is shown so clearly on the park maps, the line of high peaks, whose position must indicate the approximate former position of the watershed, is entirely restrictd to the east slope. The Grand Teton, by way of illustration, is almost three miles east of the nearest point on the present watershed, and Mount Moran is nearly five miles east of it. Most of the peaks are tied to the watershed by connecting ridges. Buck Mountain, alone of the major peaks, carries the divide, although the actual summit too is a quarter-mile east of it.

The relationships described account for the anomalous situation with reference to the east-slope canyons, which are deepest and most spectacular by far in their middle sections, whereas at their heads along the watershed they are comparatively shallow. Thus the walls of Cascade Canyon a half-mile from its mouth are from 2,000 to 3,000 feet high; a mile farther upstream they are from 3,500 to 4,500 feet high; a half-mile still farther, 5,000 feet; but from there on, as the canyon is ascended, their height decreases until at the head of the north fork (six miles above the mouth of the canyon) they terminate in cirque cliffs only a thousand feet high. Now looking backward from the watershed, one observes that Cascade Canyon is deepest in its middle part because here it passes through the belt of high peaks, with whose sheer upper faces its own walls are in places continuous. Looking in other directions, one perceives how far into the former domain of the west slope the east-slope canyons have already penetrated, with gain of length but loss of steepness, depth, and altitude; and one understands how the watershed will become progressively lower as the range approaches symmetry.

Thus, from the upfaulted Teton block, streams roughed out a distinctive mountain landscape. As we continue to observe it, we find evidence of the work of other agencies as well: frost, rain, avalanches, daily and seasonal temperature changes, and, most significant of all perhaps, the glaciers of the ice age.

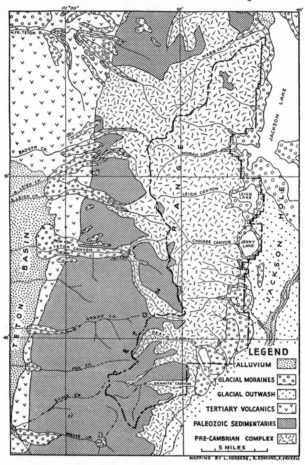

Fig. 1. Geologic map of the Teton Range (showing boundaries of the Grand Teton National Park)

Records Written in Stone

ON THE BASIS of their geologic age, the rocks of the Teton Range fall into three principal groups: the pre-Cambrian "complex," the Paleozoic sedimentaries, and the Tertiary volcanics.[1] Reference to the geologic map (fig. 1) and the block diagram (fig. 2; see following page) will make clear the distribution and position of these major rock groups.

Outcropping most widely are the pre-Cambrian rocks. The term "complex" suggests the diversity of these rocks and their varied relationships. Probably more than five hundred million years old—an antiquity beyond our comprehension—the pre-Cambrian crystallines form the core of the range, and become familiar to all Teton visitors inasmuch as they include the rock types which are most common in the park.

Resting on the pre-Cambrian as on a foundation are found the Paleozoic sedimentary strata, a succession of beds of limestone, sandstone, quartzite, and shale, having an aggregate thickness of about three thousand feet. Even to the untrained eye it is evident that this monumental pile of strata may be subdivided into a number of distinctive formations. The fossilized remains of the marine plants and animals which they contain, no less than the nature of the rocks themselves, establish the fact that the Paleozoic strata orig-

[1] Rocks of Mesozoic age are present in the range, but only at its extremities.

inated as layers of sand, mud, and limestone spread over
the floors of ancient seas. Thus in the Tetons, as throughout
much of the Rocky Mountain region, there is found a record
of the marine waters that during Paleozoic time again and
again invaded western North America, and as often with-
drew. The time required for the accumulation of these strata

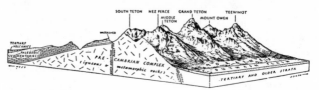

FIG. 2. GENERALIZED BLOCK DIAGRAM OF THE TETON RANGE

was perhaps two hundred fifty million years, and this vast
period of the earth's history ended about two hundred million years ago.

Overlying the older rock groups are the Tertiary volcanics, which include lavas and breccias of rhyolite and an-
desite. Except for stream and glacial deposits, these are the
youngest rocks of the range; even so, their age must be
reckoned in tens of millions of years. The outpouring of
these lavas in the Tertiary period accompanied widespread
volcanic activity which affected many other areas in the
West and Northwest, including the Yellowstone region.

Before the building of the Rocky Mountains, the Paleozoic sedimentaries extended unbrokenly over the whole
region; formerly the Tertiary volcanics were also more
widespread than now. With the rise of the Teton block and
the dissection which followed, these rocks were subjected to
vigorous weathering and erosion, especially throughout the

loftier parts of the block. Here over wide areas the sedimentaries were stripped back from the underlying crystallines, and the volcanics were similarly removed from the formations on which they rested.[2] Eventually the pre-Cambrian core was laid bare on much of the west slope, as well as more extensively along the east front of the range where the Teton fault had already in part exposed it.

With these relationships in mind, one can better comprehend the Teton scene. Throughout most of the central, alpine area, where uplift was greatest and therefore denudation most profound, the volcanics and sedimentaries have been wholly removed, and the exposed pre-Cambrian crystallines have been deeply carved into peaks and canyons. However, here and there on the margins of this central area may be noted peaks and ridges that preserve on their summits remnants of the lowermost sedimentaries, usually quartzite and limestone. To such cappings Mount Moran, Prospectors Mountain, Table Mountain, and a few other summits owe their distinctive flat tops. Toward the extremities of the range and to the west of the watershed the sedimentary strata—and in places also the volcanics—are present as a cover that, though frayed, still roofs over the crystalline foundation. Seen from the north or south the westward inclination of these formations is very evident, an impressive record of the tilt to which the Teton block was long ago subjected.

[2] Recent studies by Dr. Leland Horberg indicate that the Tertiary volcanics of the range were spread out upon the eroded crests of low folds. These folds must have resulted from mountain-building movements that affected the region long before either the volcanic activity or the uplift along the Teton fault had set in. An important part of the removal of the Paleozoic beds must have followed this early folding, inasmuch as the Tertiary volcanics in places rest directly on the pre-Cambrian rocks.

Reference has been made to the structural similarity of the Tetons to the Sierra Nevada. With respect to rocks, both ranges have in common the volcanics spread like a veneer over their west-slope formations. Otherwise they show more of lithologic dissimilarity than of resemblance. The most notable features of the Sierra landscape are largely developed in granites, those of the Tetons in a diversity of rocks, largely nongranitic. Seeking in the Sierra for an equivalent to the inclined sedimentaries of the Teton west slope, that here outline a bold topography, one finds a crumbled series of slates that weather into subdued contours. A further contrasting of Sierra and Teton land forms, as they reflect the underlying rock materials, would be of interest but would lead far afield.

Of the three predominant rock groups in the Tetons, the volcanics are scenically the least significant, but they possess a special importance in connection with the question of when the Teton block began to rise. Presumably the present volcanic remnants were once continuous with each other and with the volcanic plateaus overlapping the range on the west from the Snake River Plains, and on the north from the Pitchstone Plateau. In these adjacent areas they are still flat-lying; in the range they dip westward. It is therefore evident that the uplift and tilting responsible for the Teton Range must have occurred since the outpouring of the lavas, that is, since middle Tertiary (Miocene) time. Whether uplift began immediately after the Miocene or appreciably later is still an open question; it may have been well toward the end of the Tertiary period.

From the Jackson Hole side one may obtain a striking though distant view of the west-slope sedimentaries by looking up Avalanche Canyon, where they appear from behind the South Teton and Mount Wister. In this view their massive beds dip away toward the west, their edges encircling the canyon head in "The Wall," several hundred feet high, of a regularity so marked as to arrest the eye even when seen from a distance of fifteen or twenty miles.

However, to observe the sedimentaries to best advantage and at close range one must, of course, cross to the west slope itself. The trail connecting the heads of Cascade and Death canyons passes for several miles through or near splendid exposures. On this slope the great canyons cleave the strata to a depth of two thousand feet or more, and their cross sections appear in the canyon walls and in the sides of tabular residuals that rise from the divides. From these outcrops the geologist may collect trilobites, brachiopods, corals, and many other fossils, all of species long since vanished never to return, records of a marine fauna that flourished here millions of years ago when seas spread over the area where now stand snow-laden peaks. There are extensive coral reefs, ten thousand feet or more above sea level. Of even greater interest are the curious algal reefs that weather out of the shales at the head of Fox Creek Canyon and elsewhere along the divide and on the west slope. Knobby, globular structures several feet in diameter, they are composed of limestone deposited by primitive plants that grew in the Cambrian seas, much as do their remote descendants in the modern seas.

Sink holes and small caves are fairly common in the limestone formations of the west slope, and there is reason to believe that caves of larger size will be found.

With respect to the degree of resistance they offer to

erosion and weathering, the sedimentary formations differ within wide limits. Weak beds, particularly the shales, recede to form steps and benches along the canyon walls; resistant ones, such as the Death Canyon, Bighorn, and Madison formations, stand forth as bold and continuous cliffs. This contrast has given rise to landscape features of great diversity and beauty, some bearing striking resemblance to architectural forms. Among these the traveler may wander as through a deserted city, treading stone pavements from which his footsteps loudly reëcho, exploring mural alcoves and intersecting avenues, pausing, perhaps, in contemplation of citadels that once rose in majesty but are now collapsing into ruins beneath the weight of their own massive masonry; or he may, if he wishes, ascend the parapets of walls that have resisted the siege of time so well that their mile-long continuity is still almost unbroken. There is apparent everywhere an orderliness which we, humanwise, find suggestive of man's design, a conscious adherence to an architectural plan utilizing throughout the same long, parallel, west-slanting lines—a pattern imposed on all these landscape forms by the initial tilt of the Teton block.

Following these lines of composition the eye is inevitably at last drawn eastward, where, across the divide, tower the Tetons. Their fascination is irresistible. Awful in their immensity, jagged and fantastic in form, they brood over the silent city of the west slope like a group of abandoned pagan gods. We approach, eager to learn what factors are responsible for peaks that display such amazing individuality.

As has already been pointed out, the Teton peaks have been developed out of pre-Cambrian crystalline rocks. Perhaps in their structural content may be found one factor contributing toward their uniqueness of form; the relation between rock and topography would appear too close for mere coincidence. When engineers sketched out boundaries for the park and drew lines enclosing the most rugged country, they outlined also, in a general way, the outcrops of the crystalline rocks. Go where you will in the Tetons, so long as you traverse these most ancient of terranes, your steps lead you through scenes of majesty; leave them and you enter landscapes that however beautiful are far more subdued. Were you to start at Teton Pass and travel northward, your course would offer no great difficulties as far as the vicinity of Prospectors Mountain, but here, where the sedimentary beds terminate and the underlying crystallines come to the surface, the landscape abruptly changes character. Looking northward across the canyon gulf you would behold peak rising beyond peak, all of a new and highly distinctive type, far sharper and steeper of slope than those hitherto encountered, with profiles of splintered rock, unsoftened by verdure, each springing aloft with startling suddenness—peaks that, it has often been said, look as peaks should look. Here your explorations would probably end— or, should you resolve to continue, would really begin.

What then are these crystalline rocks? Contrary to general belief they include but little true granite. To the geologist this statement cannot be surprising, knowing as he does that granite rarely lends itself to forms sharp as these. Originally lavas, sediments, and igneous rocks, the pre-Cambrian terranes have been folded, sheared, and recrystallized until their original character is almost or wholly lost, and the geologist must now designate them as gneiss, schist, and pegmatite—rock types which, if unfamiliar to most persons, are at least not difficult to distinguish once learned. The exceptional topography of these mountains must be considered a logical product of exceedingly rapid weathering and erosion in rocks of these types under the conditions imposed by high altitudes.

The enormous pressure and heat which altered the rocks so profoundly were possibly exerted in connection with mountain building and volcanism in remote pre-Cambrian time. These rocks may, therefore, be the "roots" of an ancient generation of mountains, long since worn away, compared to which the present Tetons are youthful indeed.

In the gneiss and pegmatite, light-colored minerals, quartz and feldspar, predominate to an extent that determines the prevailing tone of the range itself, which is gray where the rock is freshly exposed and tinged with brown where weathered. The schists, mainly of the micaceous and hornblende varieties, are for the most part dark green or black in color. Mineralogic uniformity is the rule, and the less common minerals are rarely seen, though crystals of garnet are sometimes found in the pegmatite outcrops of Glacier Gulch, Garnet Canyon, and elsewhere, some up to three inches in diameter.

In details of texture and pattern the rocks show almost endless variety, providing an inexaustible study and at the same time contributing by their beauty to one's enjoyment of the mountains.

In almost every outcrop and even in rock fragments found along the trail, close observation may reveal such features as folds and faults which reproduce in miniature the major geological structures of whole mountain ranges. In many places the gneisses are strikingly banded, and, like the

schists, exhibit highly complicated crumpling. Everywhere
the rocks give evidence of how tremendous were the forces
that long ago fractured them, made them flow as though
plastic, or recrystallized them.

The crystals are commonly large and well developed, so
that it is easy to determine the mineralogic composition of
the rock.

The interest of most visitors springs from the clean, bright
appearance of the rocks where their outcrops glint in the
sun, or from their sheer beauty where banded or where stud-
ded with plumelike aggregates of mica crystals. Many, however, must wonder at the complicated patterns to be seen
in places where rocks penetrate each other in intricate fashion, relationships which give the geologist information on
the relative age of the formations.

Collectively the rocks make up a complex series dipping
steeply eastward; in a few places, as in Death and Waterfalls canyons, the dips are westward. Whichever the direction of the dip, the rock takes on a sheeted structure, or
cleavage, set, so to speak, on edge. Attacked by the elements,
frost in particular, the rock splits off along the structure or
irregularly across it, like well-grained wood. The peaks and
ridges thus developed splintered summits, pinnacles of bristling sharpness, and faces that approach verticality and in
places actually overhang. On bare upper slopes, as on the
north walls of Avalanche and Garnet canyons, the grain
stands out to form tremendous ridges which are separated by avalanche-swept couloirs. Where such features
reach the summit of Mount St. John they give rise to a
saw-toothed crest. The pegmatite and gneiss, because they
withstand weathering and erosion better than the schists,

are usually found to outcrop along the ridges, in the pinnacles, and to compose the greater part of the huge peak
bodies.

To an important degree the tactics employed by mountaineers are controlled by this factor of inclined cleavage.
In scaling the east faces of Mount Owen, Teewinot, Nez
Perce, and many another peak, it is necessary to go up
smooth, slabby surfaces that require a climbing technique
quite unlike that employed in scaling these same peaks
from the west. On the east faces the alpinist climbs with
the grain of the rock; on the west, against it. Routes from
intermediate directions may involve either of these situations or, more likely, both.

Joints—the straight fractures which are present in rocks
almost everywhere—are conspicuous features of the pre-
Cambrian crystallines, and where highly developed may
govern the topography to an extent equaling or exceeding
the cleavage. Not uncommonly single fissures can be traced
continuously for hundreds of feet. Regardless of extent,
they furnish innumerable planes of entry into which air
and moisture can penetrate and, through chemical activity
or through freezing, perform the "secret ministries" that
lead eventually to rock disruption. Certain nearly vertical
joint systems trending parallel to the main east–west canyons have greatly facilitated the erosional work of streams
and glaciers, and are in no small measure responsible for
the development of the tremendous walls that bound the
Teton canyons.

Individual crystals in the pegmatite may be as much as
several inches in diameter. In weathering, these produce
roughened rock surfaces and protrusions to which the rub-

A FAULT IN THE TETON GNEISS OCCUPIED BY A LAYER OF PEGMATITE

FOLDED STRUCTURES IN THE TETON GNEISS

BLACK DIKE
ON THE MIDDLE TETON

NORTH FACE
OF THE GRAND TETON

Photos, Jim Olson

ber soles or the *tricouni* nails of the mountaineer's shoes tenaciously adhere, enabling him to scale rock faces that have every appearance of being impregnable. From the mountaineer's standpoint the rock of the Tetons is admirable. Brush, talus, and loose boulders he must assuredly expect to contend with, but decomposed or crumbling rock is virtually unknown, one explanation of the comparatively few climbing accidents in the region.

No features in the Teton range excite more curiosity than do the remarkable black bands in the sides of three of the peaks. One such is on the southeast face of Mount Moran; another on the south slope of the Grand Teton; a third on the east face of the Middle Teton. So regular as to look artificial, they cause much speculation, a common conjecture being that they are open cracks in the mountain. They have even been supposed to be stairways, constructed for the convenience of tourists. Each summer a few energetic souls scramble onto Mount Moran to investigate firsthand the mysterious black streak in its face, and they bring down specimens of a fine-grained, very heavy black rock that, they are told, is diabase.

These bands result from cross-section exposures of dikes, the tabular structures formed through molten rock (magma) rising into a fissure and there solidifying. The Teton dikes might well provide text book illustrations, so striking is the contrast between the black intrusions and the light-colored rock they cut. For all their apparent freshness they are ancient structures, formed in pre-Cambrian time and hence long antedating the range; and like the other crystallines they were exposed when the Teton block, after uplift, was stripped of its cover of younger rocks. As they cut through the peaks they outcrop conspicuously on both sides, and each may be traced down the west slope to the point where it passes from sight beneath the sedimentary beds. Microscopic study shows the diabase of the three dikes to be very similar, suggesting that perhaps they were formed at the same time through the upwelling of magma from a common source. Possibly they connect with each other or with some larger, deep-seated mass of similar rock.

Estimates of the width of these dikes by visitors vary astonishingly, and illustrate the difficulty newcomers experience in trying to comprehend the scale of mountains. The Mount Moran dike, for example, has been assigned widths ranging from 10 to 1,000 feet. It actually measures 125 feet at the base of the peak. The Grand Teton dike is from 40 to 60 feet wide, and the Middle Teton dike from 20 to 40 feet.

Interesting topographic features result along the line of outcrop of the dikes. Where more resistant than the rocks that enclose them, a situation best illustrated on Mount Moran, they stand in relief as straight, high walls; where less resistant, they form narrow depressions. In the groove of the Middle Teton dike, snow often persists until late summer, so that a white band instead of a black one marks its trace.

The Grand Teton dike gives rise to a gulch so striking as to be a major feature of the peak. It cuts straight through the steep south slope and isolates from the main body of the mountain a thin rock wedge several miles long. Once a veritable knife blade, this wedge is now shattered into bristling pinnacles, the more prominent of which are Disappointment Peak, Teepe Pillar, and the Red Sentinel. During the ice age the dike trough actually sheltered a small glacier

that widened it and, at the north base of Teepe Pillar, excavated a cirque.

Affording as it does a natural avenue by which to reach
the west face of the Grand Teton, the dike depression has
been repeatedly traversed by mountaineers; and the dikes
on the Middle Teton and Mount Moran have similarly provided climbing routes.

Often it has been asked, are there no "minerals" in this
range?—meaning of course are there no "ores," for in the
prospector's parlance no notice is taken of any minerals
except those that can be marketed. Ores do occur here, but
so far as known most of the deposits are unimportant. Near
the head of Death Canyon Trail are several old prospect
holes and two abandoned log cabins that give evidence of
an unsuccessful attempt, made in 1907 and 1908, to develop
some small silver-lead deposits. The Cambrian beds contain iron ore in the form of more or less impure oölitic
hematite that outcrops in an irregular line along the divide
and on the west slope; it has not been exploited and probably never will be because of its remoteness from markets.
Asbestos of high grade occurs in the north end of the range,
near Berry Creek, and has been mined. The talc from which
the early Indians of the region carved bowls is said to have
come from quarries in the northwestern part of the range.
There are traces of molybdenite and copper-containing minerals in the pre-Cambrian rocks of the alpine region. Down
on the west slope, the Carboniferous formations, especially
the Phosphoria beds of Permian age, contain extensive beds
of black phosphate rock that constitute a reserve of real
value. The placer gold so widespread throughout the Snake
River gravels of Jackson Hole, yet so exasperatingly diffi-

cult of recovery because of its fineness, has apparently all
been washed down from the hills to the north and northeast, not from the Tetons. From early times to our own, this
"flour gold" has lured prospectors—and eluded them. The
"old-timer" who posted the following notice on Deadman's
Bar had probably been made wise by experience:

> Payin gold will never be found here
> No matter how many men tries
> Theres some enough to begile one
> Like tanglefoot paper does flies.

Thus, compared with many ranges, the Tetons are quite
barren, providentially so with respect to the conservation
of their greatest resources. The true wealth of these mountains lies in their snow-clad summits, their lakes and streams
and forests, and in the tonic qualities of their air. These
lodes will never play out. Had the Tetons contained "minerals" in any quantity, neither their ruggedness nor their
beauty could have protected them. The forests would have
been cut for mine timbers and lumber, the peaks scarred by
shafts and the gopherings of prospectors, and the canyons
however steep invaded by roads blasted from the rock. As
it was, when the National Park Service in 1929 assumed
stewardship of the Tetons it found the east slope of the range
still a wilderness almost as continuous and splendid as when
John Colter, the first white man to see it, passed this way
a century and a quarter ago.

In sad contrast to this, the opposite slope, outside the
park, has been despoiled of much of its original charm, not
through mining so much as through overgrazing by cattle
and, especially, sheep. Each summer the sheep are driven

up the mountainsides in great flocks to the high open country above timber line, where, up to the park boundary (the watershed), they leisurely fatten, moving through the flowery alpine meadows like a blight that destroys all in its path. This slope was formerly the summer range of deer, elk, moose, and bighorn, but the numbers of these animals have been greatly reduced, and there is little chance of their recovery so long as the forage is thus usurped and laid waste, the range on the steep east slope being far too limited to support many animals. The bighorn in particular have had their ranks thinned, probably in part by diseases contracted from the domestic sheep. They are rarely seen now except at the extreme north end of the range, where a band of less than a hundred survivors is still occasionally reported. Better than any other animals the bighorns typify the Tetons, yet they must inevitably soon disappear unless steps are taken to exclude their domestic brethren from the west slope of the range.

The Glacial Experience

A MILLION OR MORE years ago the ice age began. In terms of earth history this most recent of the earth's great glacial times is known as the Pleistocene period. Whether it was inaugurated by lowered temperatures or increased snowfall, or both, is not yet clear; nor can a satisfactory explanation be given of the causes underlying these climatic changes. In the Tetons, as in other lofty ranges of the West, there came on very gradually a time when summer melting no longer removed the snowfall of winter, and an increasing excess of snow accumulated in the canyon heads and about the high peaks. Compacted under their own weight, and through subtle molecular changes that converted snowflakes into crystalline ice, the fields of snow became glaciers, whose tongues moved slowly down to lower altitudes, utilizing as their channels the great stream-cut canyons. In time, every important canyon in the Tetons was appropriated by an ice stream, fed at sources along the crest of the range or among the peaks, or both.

The Alaskan ranges which are today burdened with ice and snow enable us to visualize the Teton Range as it must have appeared in this period—the geological yesterday.

Development of the glaciers was profoundly influenced by the high peaks east of the watershed. These peaks, because of their great altitude, formed radial glacial systems of their own that contributed ice to the valley glaciers moving eastward past their feet. Even glacial tongues which descended the west faces of these peaks were, lower down, diverted northward or southward and became tributary to the east-flowing valley glaciers. Additional factors emphasized still further the advantages of this slope, so that the glaciers here were well nourished and vigorous, and the records they inscribed are accordingly striking. In marked contrast, the valley glaciers on the west slope of the range remained comparatively feeble, for their sources were limited to the watershed which at no point is much higher than 11,000 feet.

Within what is now Grand Teton National Park, not only did certain of the glaciers almost or entirely fill their canyons to the rim, but most of them eventually came to occupy the full length of the canyons and pushed beyond their mouths onto the floor of Jackson Hole, where, unconfined, they deployed widely. Where Jackson Lake is now situated, there lay a great sluggish field of ice resulting from the confluence of adjacent piedmont glaciers, with, perhaps, contributions from the Yellowstone Plateau to the north.

Through the millenniums of the ice age the glaciers were now extended, now reduced. At times they may have disappeared altogether. It is not necessary to attempt here the unraveling of these complexities, however intriguing to the student of glacial times. We shall consider only the glaciers of the later stages in their role as sculptors of mountains.

Whatever the climatic changes that brought on the ice age, they were again reversed a relatively few thousand years ago, so that the ice by degrees loosened its grip on the range; and as the glaciers shrank headward, making their last stand in the deeper recesses of the canyons and on the shadowy north slopes, where some of their remnants may still be found, it was a profoundly altered mountain range which again lay open to the sun, and which the forests and flowers and wild creatures reclaimed. For everywhere were impressed on the landscape new features, making for heightened grandeur and beauty.

How changed were the canyons! Gone were the narrow, jagged clefts of preglacial times, and in their stead had been carved open, broad-floored chasms with walls awesome alike for their stupendous height and for their sheerness, at their heads terminating in groups of amphitheater-like cirques whose enclosing bare walls stand hundreds or thousands of feet high. Through corridors of such grandeur the traveler mounts, step by step, to the spacious mountain halls of the high country.

Most convincing is the evidence in each canyon of the severity with which the rock-shod glaciers of the ice age, like great flexible files, gouged out, deepened, and straightened the channels down which they moved. Though thousands of years have elapsed since the ice vanished, here and there on the crystalline pavements and walls are preserved areas of the burnished or grooved surfaces it produced, the "autographs of the glaciers." On these the sunlight glances, at times almost blindingly. In places trees have as yet failed to gain foothold on the polished rock. Formerly of wide extent, the glaciated surfaces are being destroyed by weathering, flaking off or separating from the underlying rock in thin brown sheets that can be pried away with a knife blade.

In few mountain regions can one find as great a variety of ice-shaped canyons as here, where they range from colossal chasms more than a mile deep, whose somber depths appall one, to curious shallow gulches developed where small glaciers clung to the upper faces of the peaks, as on the east slopes of Teewinot and St. John, and the various sides of Mount Moran. The principal canyons, such as Granite, Death, Cascade, and Moran, are so tremendously deep that they cleave the range into segments, which the tributary canyons diversify with their finer, more intricate sculptural forms.

In moving down from its high sources, the ice excavated shallow hollows in the bedrock where the latter was much fractured or for other reasons was nonresistant. Depressions so produced are now occupied by small alpine lakes, of which there are scores in the range. Most of them are only a few hundred feet across, and the largest measures not more than a quarter-mile to a half-mile long. Until recently many had remained unreported, so that on explorations in the lesser-known sections of the high country rangers and mountaineers frequently chanced upon rock-rimmed tarns of whose existence the maps had given them no previous hint. Some are hung on precipitous mountainsides where it might reasonably be asserted no lake could exist; others, including those best known, lie within the canyons, either in their upper levels or inside the cirques. Such are Amphitheater Lake and Lake Solitude, both frequently visited now that they are accessible by trail. Hanging Canyon on Mount St. John contains a chain of three lakes, Lake of the Crags, Ramshead Lake, and Arrowhead Pool; in Avalanche Canyon there are two, Snowdrift Lake and Lake Taminah. Still others, presumably produced where the ice overflowed the canyons and sheared across intervening divides, are especially characteristic of high altitudes and bear little or no relationship to the canyons. These are distributed over the rock slopes and benches above timber line as irregularly as if sprinkled down on the range. Reflecting only rock, snow, sky, and cloud, the lakelets of this type, the most truly alpine of all, are thoroughly in keeping with their lonely environment.

Much larger are the piedmont lakes, of which there are six in the park—Leigh, String, Jenny, Bradley, Taggart, and Phelps—and a seventh just outside it, Jackson Lake, covering much more area than all the rest combined. Though resting on the valley floor, entirely outside the mountains, these lakes are also the handiwork of glaciers. All are ranged in a nearly straight line, close against the foot of the mountains. Three of the northerly members of this group, Leigh, String, and Jenny lakes, are linked like beads by Cottonwood Creek, which, as it continues southward, collects also the overflow streams from Bradley and Taggart lakes.

Nestled in dense forests outside the mouths of the canyons, the lakes provide a foreground of rare loveliness across which to view the mountain panorama to the west. Out of the very margins of the lakes spring the slender peaks, and every feature of their lofty summits, a mile or more above, is at times faithfully reflected in the quiet depths beneath.

Nor is their arrangement with reference to the canyons capricious or accidental. Each lake marks the place where a valley glacier, reaching out from an adjacent canyon in the range, for a time rested its cold snout upon the floor of Jackson Hole. The bouldery, heavily timbered embankments that enclose the lakes, concentric ridges over which the trails rise and fall, are moraines built up by the glaciers as they carried forward and deposited along their melting margins outside the canyons great quantities of rock débris. String Lake, an expansion of the stream connecting Leigh and Jenny lakes, owes its existence to an obstructing gravel deposit built up by glacial streams from the north.

With a few hours at his disposal the visitor may climb the Teton Glacier Trail or some one of the canyon trails to a point of vantage from which he can look down upon a section of this chain of lakes. He will then readily note that each lake lies outside the mouth of a canyon, and that it occupies a moraine basin. Each overflows through a low place on the rim of its basin, its outlet cascading to the valley floor beneath.

Within the moraines outside of Granite Canyon and Glacier Gulch, meadows replace the lakes once present, the latter having been filled or drained. This must eventually happen to all the lakes, though for the deeper ones such fate may be long deferred. And in view of their relatively small size some of these piedmont lakes are of exceptional depth. Recent accurate soundings indicate that Jackson Lake has a maximum depth exceeding 400 feet; Leigh Lake, 250 feet; String Lake, 10 feet; Jenny Lake, 226 feet; Bradley Lake, 93 feet; Taggart Lake, 31 feet; and Phelps Lake, 158 feet.

In most places these lakes are bordered by weathered glacial boulders, eroded from the moraines. The east margin of Leigh Lake, however, has a fine beach of white feldspathic sand that makes this lake suitable for swimming.

Standing shoulder-deep in Leigh Lake are two small morainal hills that form Mystic and Boulder isles, the latter so called because on it is an immense glacial boulder, the largest in the valley. The basal portion is buried, but the exposed part is forty feet through in one direction and ninety-five in another, and it rises to a height of fifty-three feet. That it was once even larger is shown by a surrounding fringe of smaller boulders sloughed from its sides. Since it is higher than the adjacent pines, this rock stands out as a landmark visible from all elevations in the northern part of the range. Despite its huge size and weight, it was doubtless transported for miles by the glacier that once occupied Indian Paintbrush Canyon. Up in the range boulders almost as large may be seen at the edge of Teton Glacier, forming a part of the moraine which that glacier is now building; and resting on the ice field itself, riding slowly along with it toward the moraine, are many other great boulders, some with diameters of from thirty to forty feet.

Significant also are the moraines with respect to the Teton forests. These are part of a timber zone that encircles Jackson Hole. The zone is miles in width except on the west, where, in passing up the steep Teton front, it narrows to a mere strip. At low elevations the forests extend uninterruptedly; at higher ones they fringe out at timber line, which in the Tetons is an irregular but very distinct line at from 10,000 to 11,000 feet. As for the lower limit of the forests, in most places the trees have pressed down to the edge of the valley floor, where, as if acknowledging here the sovereignty of the sagebrush, they abruptly stop. Here and there may be noted a lodgepole pine that, more daring than the rest, stands alone in the sagebrush.

But at the base of the Tetons the forests have advanced out into the valley a mile or more. This they have done almost exclusively on moraines, extending only to their limits. Thus the morainal embankments of the mountain front are emphasized not alone by relief, but also by the forest cover which effectively sets them off against the gray plains.

Forests on the moraines, sagebrush on the outwash plains —that is the rule, and the situation is due to the underlying terrane. The moraines consist of heterogeneous rock materials carried out from the range by the ancient glaciers. Because of their compactness they retain the moisture essential to forest growth; they are also rich in the minerals that are likewise necessary. Quite different are the plains. Largely made up of quartzite cobbles spread over the valley by glacial streams that formerly flowed in from the north, the plains are both barren and dry. Therefore the forests have kept to the mountains and moraines, leaving the plains to the hardier sage. In places one can step from moraine to the gravels which overlap it, and in so doing pass from lodgepole forest to sagebrush. Thus accurately does flora reflect the geological pattern.

We return to the Teton canyons. Large or small, they are all vocal with cascades and waterfalls that provide a pervasive overtone for all other sounds.

Most of the falls far back in the range are of glacial origin. Where the glaciers deepened the main canyons more than their tributaries, the latter were left hanging, with resultant waterfalls when the ice melted away. Also, in the rock over which they moved, the glaciers encountered inequalities which erosion brought into relief, producing gigantic steps along the canyon floors. Down these "cyclopean stairways" the streams now course, with as many falls or cascades as there are successive levels.

Finest of these waterfalls are Wilderness Falls, in upper Waterfalls Canyon, and Twin Falls, that, just below the outlet of Lake Taminah, leaps with divided stream out of the high north head of Avalanche Canyon.

Other waterfalls are marginal with reference to the mountains, hung all up and down the east front of the range as though on display, one or several in the mouth of each canyon. Such falls may be older than the others, having originated before the later stages of the ice age; yet one may suppose that in the glacial reshaping of the canyons any waterfalls already present would be greatly changed, and that these falls too came to their present appearance and position through the agency of ice.

The origin of the marginal waterfalls is not entirely clear. In the sculpturing of the range, the downcutting of the canyons appears to have lagged behind the deepening of Jackson Hole, which went on concurrently, perhaps because the rock in the range is much harder than that underlying the basin, or because the Teton block was in the meantime subjected to renewed uplifts. Either cause would occasion the situation which produced the falls—abrupt steepening of the canyons where they open into Jackson Hole. To speak geologically, the canyons are hanging with reference to the valley, in some instances only a few hundred feet, as with Cascade and Death canyons, and in others more than a thousand feet, as with the canyons of the Mount St. John group. In approaching these declivities the streams quicken their pace, anticipating perhaps the adventure of leaving behind the scenes wherein their fortunes have hitherto been laid; finally, roaring in high excitement, each hurls itself headlong through one exultant leap after another down toward the valley below. More composedly but nonetheless with eager course, they then move away from the mountains and across the flats of Jackson Hole to mingle their waters and destinies with those of the Snake.

The contribution that the waterfalls make to the wild beauty of the Tetons can no more be measured than can the values of snow fields, clouds, and shadows. As their loveliness charms the eye so their voices dispel all loneliness. Within the portals of any canyon you may choose to enter awaits a waterfall or a cascade, perhaps several. Their crashing music, reëchoed between canyon walls, thunders a welcome to the high country. And at time of departure the mountain voices last heard are again those of the waterfalls, now in farewell.

As if Nature had been mindful of those unable to enter the range, many of the waterfalls are so situated as to be visible from out in the valley. Passing through Jackson Hole one may glimpse them, as in canyon after canyon they come into sight: Twin Falls, Bannock Falls, Glacier Falls, Broken Falls, Hidden Cascades, Ribbon Cascades, Wilderness Falls, and many others. It is a silent review, for at such a distance their sound is not heard, nor can one detect any flow or wavering in the silver-white lines of their streaming traceries. After a warm summer day, however, the volume of each waterfall is noticeably augmented. And how quickly the effect of an afternoon thunderstorm among the high peaks manifests itself in this display. Of a sudden each waterfall and cascade stands out against its canyon rim with new and clearer emphasis; refreshed, it gleams more brightly than before, though it still may be overhung by somber storm clouds. Is it imagination, or can one now really hear their far-off murmur?

Mountain glaciers sculpture most boldly at their very

HIDDEN FALLS IN CASCADE CANYON

THE GRAND TETON,
WITH THE TETON GLACIER AT THE BASE OF THE PEAK

Photo, Ed Riddell

SEDIMENTARY BEDS AT THE HEAD OF AVALANCHE CANYON

Photo, Ed Riddell

WEST SLOPE OF THE TETONS, LEFT TO RIGHT:
MOUNT OWEN, THE GRAND, MIDDLE AND SOUTH TETONS

PERMANENT SNOWFIELD
ON MOUNT OWEN

GLACIAL MORAINE AT
THE BASE OF MOUNT TEEWINOT

Photos, Jim Olson

sources. Many of the heads of the Teton glaciers were clustered about the highest peaks, and here the rock, because of jointing and upended cleavage, lent itself with peculiar effectiveness to glacial erosion. Quarrying deep into the slopes on which they rested, the glaciers steepened their headwalls to the sheerest of mountain faces. The individual peaks, attacked in this fashion from several sides, were cut back and faceted like colossal gems—most strikingly so, Buck Mountain, the Grand Teton, Teewinot, and Mount Moran.

A further result of the glacial sculpturing was to isolate each peak more completely than before, and to sharpen its profile. Through attack on connecting ridges Mount Owen, for example, was completely separated from Teewinot on the east and nearly so from the Grand Teton on the south, leaving unreduced a thin, ragged connecting arête. Yet even among these most rugged peaks there are a few restricted areas of gentle slope. These may be remnants of a landscape antedating the last advance of the ice that here escaped obliteration because of a lofty position on the divides, above and between the glaciers. Such perhaps are the surfaces in the broad pass between the Middle and Grand Tetons, on the beveled top of Disappointment Peak, on the flat bench west of Teewinot, and elsewhere.

Small glaciers, tributary to those occupying the main canyons, bit into the east–west intercanyon ridges, especially from the north, so vigorously as to break them down at one or several places along the east front of the mountains, to produce a number of forepeaks. Of these, Teewinot and Nez Perce are the best representatives. The latter peak, together with Cloudveil Dome and several other summits, is isolated from the ridge running eastward from the South Teton. In the Mount St. John group, as throughout the alpine region, the tendency to develop one or several forepeaks from each of the intercanyon ridges is evident, so that on the map the summits appear roughly grouped in double rank.

Thus were produced profiles that have made the Tetons distinguished representatives of a mountain type that is rare: toothed peaks, small of summit area and with precipitous, even concave, sides—peaks combining great altitude with spectacular boldness of form. And the distinctive features of each peak (for no two are alike) may be understood by observing the distribution and character of the glaciers that sculptured it, as well as the nature of the rock in which they worked.

Landscapes in the Making

IN THE MAKING of mountains as in all else, Nature is an unsparing self-critic, never satisfied, never considering her task finished. Could human life flow on as continuously as do the mountain streams, we should discover that the Teton peaks and canyons, in common with landscapes everywhere, pass ceaselessly on from form to form. In mountains lofty and rugged as these, change proceeds with such relative swiftness that in revisiting familiar scenes year after year we unerringly detect its traces.

Since the range in the main became free of ice, streams have reoccupied the canyons, and resumption of their former erosional activity is indicated by the sharp trenches through which in places they flow—gorges cut into the ice-scoured floors of the canyons. Where the streams empty into lakes, deltas are making their appearance. One that may be viewed from the trail is the little forested delta built out from the west shore of Jenny Lake by Cascade Creek. Delta Lake, in Glacier Gulch, derives its name from the deposit that has already greatly reduced its area. In several instances postglacial time has sufficed for the complete filling or draining of lakes once present. Their former position and extent are now indicated by meadows, which, as they cease to be swampy, are being invaded by the forests of the surrounding moraines.

Most evident of the recent geologic changes are those

wrought by gravity, aided by frost, which is effective at high altitudes where the daily range of temperature is great. On many peaks and canyons the steep faces resulting from glacial erosion could not be maintained, especially where the rock was much fissured, and these faces collapsed. Shed masses of rock accumulated below, to form talus heaps which eventually assumed enormous proportions—now the homes of innumerable conies and marmots. The peaks and canyon walls are almost continuously banked with such detritus; the faces towering above, whence the rocks fell, are scarred and furrowed by continually enlarging couloirs. On the north face of Nez Perce is a gigantic hourglass, its upper portion two converging couloirs, its lower portion the symmetrical talus cone of rocks fallen from these couloirs.

In places the canyons are so encumbered with loose talus that the streams lose themselves in it, and for long distances flow out of sight and even out of hearing. Talus encroaches on most of the alpine lakes, and by its growth several have been almost obliterated, or have been divided in two, as has Ramshead Lake. Elsewhere, because of compacted talus dams across their canyon courses, streams have formed ponds and meadows, the haunts of the moose.

The rock falls that left these records probably occurred on the grandest scale in the period immediately following removal of support from the over-steepened cliffs, that is, as the glaciers of the ice age melted back out of the canyons. Yet, as the mountaineer well knows, the Teton Range is still the home of rock falls, and only he who has ventured into the realms beyond timber line, as on Mount Moran or among the Three Tetons, can appreciate how frequent they are, and how impressive. Incessantly boulders rattle from the cliffs and sweep the couloirs, leaving their trails across the snow fields. At times single rocks launch imposing slides. Such ceaseless plucking undermines larger rock masses, and great are the falls which result when entire crags or pinnacles fail of support. The strategy of a mountaineer's ascent may hinge on the problem of reducing to a minimum the hazard of falling rocks. First and foremost of the commandments to beginning climbers is this: shun the couloirs whenever possible, in favor of the far safer open ridges.

The following is an account of a rock fall that was witnessed under unusually favorable conditions by a large number of people; it is quoted from the author's notes made shortly after the occurrence:

"July 7, 1934. This morning at 9:05 a tremendous roar burst forth across Jenny Lake. Believing a fall of great magnitude must have occurred I ran from the ranger station to the shore. The roar swelled to even grander volume, yet I could not at first tell from what point in the mountains it was coming.

"Then across the lake and 2,000 feet above it, on Mount St. John, a telltale white cloud appeared within the mouth of Hanging Canyon. Compact and dense it grew till it nearly filled the space between Symmetry Spire and St. John, and it hung close to the latter in a manner indicating that rocks must be coming down its south side.

"Everyone in the campground had by this time gathered at the lake, some to photograph the cloud and others to watch it through field glasses. Unlike ordinary clouds this one appeared curiously heavy and sluggish. Seven or eight minutes from the time when the roar started it began to abate, and now became audible cannon-like reports produced by impacts of huge boulders which, though two miles distant, could be seen appearing out of the cloud and hurtling down the mountain. Doubtless the field between them was combed by smaller rocks not visible so far. Watchers with field glasses reported seeing several pines struck headlong.

"By my watch twelve minutes elapsed before the roar completely died away, except for occasional faint percussions, but the cloud, which eventually overtopped St. John and rose against the sky, was not dissipated for perhaps half an hour. In time the peculiarly unpleasant smell of pulverized rock drifted over to us.

"Three hours later I climbed up the path of the rock fall and circled around the upper portion where the rocks were still rattling and raising clouds. The fall had resulted from collapse of the west face of a summit pinnacle on St. John. Though the mass fell toward the west, it descended a series of spiraling couloirs that eventually shot it out toward the southeast, where, in its final plunge, it came into full view from Jenny Lake. At the bottom of precipices in the couloirs, rocks had struck with impacts so terrific that many had crumbled. Hence the cloud we had seen. I gathered up handfuls of the fine white powder, mostly feldspar. At the base of the lowest cliff the boulders had sprayed out and swept the full width of the lower slopes. Here the mountainside appeared as though bombarded by artillery, hundreds of ragged holes marking the spots where rocks had struck. Fresh dirt and sod were strewn about, together with wreckage of trees. Boulders previously lodged here were in many instances knocked out of position, shattered, or driven into the ground. Several rocks had descended to within a few hundred yards of Jenny Lake, tearing violently into the underbrush and forest before coming to a stop."

Trees growing on the mountain slopes are very commonly scarred and battered on their upper sides, from being struck by falling boulders.

Through ascent of a peak one gains understanding of how many rock falls originate, for the indications of rapid weathering are more pronounced with increase of altitude, and on the very summits the agencies of disruption appear to have concentrated with greatest severity. The snow which never wholly disappears from the mountaintops melts in the afternoon warmth, providing moisture that percolates into crevices and there freezes at night, when the peaks through radiation lose heat and become intensely cold. So great is the expansive force exerted by freezing water that with constant repetition of the temperature changes, day after day through year after year, rock masses even though enormously large are slowly pried loose from the mountain. By this process every mountaintop has been split and shattered, and the extreme summits of most of the peaks are covered with angular blocks that conceal beneath them the bedrock from which they were derived. Urged little by little toward the brink of the near-by precipices, most will eventually topple over. Perhaps some of the Teton summits were formerly much sharper than now, but have been blunted by such attack. On Teewinot, Mount Owen, and many of the needles in the range the summits are still clean blades of rock so slender and pointed that most boulders quarried from them cannot remain in place but plunge at once into the chasms beneath. The upper ledges of the mountains are everywhere encumbered with frost-riven rocks, and the climber must be watchful lest he grasp a rock that may pull away or one so precariously balanced that at a touch it becomes dislodged. Safety may be had only at the cost of eternal vigilance, and every hold must be tested before trusted. On the other hand, largely through the widening of cracks, there are produced those fissures and chimneys which have enabled climbers to scale rock faces which would otherwise have proved impregnable.

Of Nature's many artisans, avalanches or snowslides are the workers whose craftsmanship in the sculpturing of mountains is most likely to pass unrecognized. This is especially true in the Tetons, where avalanche occurrence is largely restricted to winter and spring, seasons in which the region of the high peaks is rarely entered. Yet every year countless boulders are swept down from the slopes by avalanches, and thus additional quotas are added to those already accumulated mainly through rock falls. As the snow melts from beneath them, avalanche-borne rocks may be let down on top of other larger boulders, or otherwise be curiously and precariously perched. At lower altitudes avalanches most emphatically demonstrate their power, for so irresistible is their descent that dense forests prove impotent to swerve or noticeably to retard them. Some of the lower slopes are treeless because avalanches have removed all forest growth or kept it from gaining foothold; on others, for example on the east face of Teewinot, avalanches have reduced the forest to remnants, with timber left standing only on the ridges, in vertical strips. Through such sweeping of débris and forests from the mountainsides new rock surfaces are exposed to the attack of other disruptive agencies.

Though elsewhere in the Jackson Hole country avalanches

have again and again snuffed out lives, in the Tetons such tragedies have naturally been limited to the Teton Pass region, at least so far as they concern human beings. In the winter the road over this pass is the main and often the sole artery of communication between the valley and the outside world, and hence when passable it is traversed by sleighs and cars freighted with mail, express, passengers, and all else that goes into or out of the isolated community. The record of narrow escapes and accidents that have occurred along this road, as a result of avalanches "running," is a long one. Among the high peaks farther north, where slides are even more dangerous, men have thus far had little occasion for getting in their paths. Not so the wild creatures, which undoubtedly are often overtaken by this swift white doom. Bodies of mountain sheep have been found several times under conditions pointing to avalanche tragedies. In the spring of 1934, on an early-season trip, a mountaineer descending Teewinot in a fresh avalanche track came upon the body of a bull moose that had been literally torn apart.

On the upper mountain slopes and summits snow does not gather in winter to the extent one might suppose. Even from January to March, when the fall is heaviest, the peaks are not everywhere white, for their heights are wind-swept and the steeper rock faces shed the dry snow. After every heavy snowfall, the roar of avalanches is heard throughout the range.

Perhaps the snowfall on the summits is actually less than on the lower slopes. Along the forested mountain front, from Jenny Lake northward, undrifted snow accumulates in winter to maximum depths of five or six feet.

When in December, 1935, three climbers ascended the Grand Teton, they were able to leave their skis at the head of Garnet Canyon and continue on foot, from this point on encountering scarcely more snow than in spring or late fall. They reported that the ascent could probably have been made even by routes more difficult than the traditional one they had followed.

Snow avalanched into the cirques and canyons builds up in these sheltered situations the huge banks that persist all summer, especially against cliffs facing away from the sun. Except for such seasonal contributions of snow the glaciers could not now exist, and we may assume that during the ice age avalanches similarly but on a larger scale nourished the huge glaciers that then occupied the canyons.

April frees the waterfalls and mountain streams, which rapidly increase in volume until late June or July, when the melting of the snow fields likewise reaches a maximum. During these months, and even later, the streams find their courses in the upper canyons blocked by great banks of snow, but, scarcely pausing, they pass on beneath them through glistening tunnels or arching bridges of snow. Though in late summer the mountain streams may dwindle, they never disappear, for at their sources in the cirques some snow fields last through even the hottest season. Out on the floor of Jackson Hole, however, it often happens that the thirsty gravels drink Cottonwood Creek entirely dry.

On a warm, sunshiny day the amount of water released from the snow fields hourly increases, and in the course of the day the streams grow in volume till the mountains seem almost to tremble from the swelling thereof. The rise in their levels reaches a peak in the afternoon, at which time the bordering meadows that were dry when crossed in the morning may be under water.

But when the sky is overcast these same streams do not noticeably change in volume during the day; their chants then remain subdued, and pitched in minor key, expressive of the day's more serious mood. However, a rainfall at their sources may perchance suddenly quicken them to new life, causing them again to lift their voices in tumultuous chorus.

At the heads of a few streams are found the glaciers. Though few and diminutive as compared with their ancestors of the ice age, they are nevertheless responsible for geologic activities that are not inconsiderable, and in themselves they are of great interest. At least seven or eight in number, the Teton glaciers range in length from a half-mile to almost a mile, and are confined to the east slope, occuring several miles east of the watershed at altitudes of between 10,000 and 11,500 feet. Here, in an environment otherwise hostile, they find existence possible because of the shade afforded by the high peaks and because of the prevailing southwest winds which drift the light, dry snow of winter over the divide and concentrate it in their basins. With the exception of Falling Ice Glacier, the Teton glaciers all face north or east, and lie at the base of peaks whose walls, rising in sheer faces to the south and west, furnish the shadows without which the glaciers would long since have vanished.

Middle Teton Glacier, the most southerly of these ice bodies, is a narrow glacial tongue that closely hugs the basal north cliffs of the peak after which it is named.

Teton Glacier occupies the huge east-facing cirque between the two highest peaks in the range, the Grand Teton and Mount Owen. It is by far the best known of the glaciers, and the recently constructed Glacier Trail makes it one of the most accessible ice bodies in the country. Half a mile below is Delta Lake, which serves as a settling basin for the sediment carried down from the glacier and which gets its name from the growing deposit that has robbed it already of one-third its area. The water of this lake is usually deep green and nearly opaque from suspended rock flour. That not all the sediment carried into the lake is deposited there is evident from the fact that even at the foot of the range, below Glacier Falls, the water of Glacier Creek is usually milky in appearance, and gritty.

Every summer Teton Glacier is visited by hundreds of visitors who, after an hour or two spent in its exploration, peering down crevasses and moulins, scrambling over its moraines, and examining the many glacial tables that give the appearance of having sprung like mushrooms from its surface, leave with a better understanding of glacial phenomena than could be gained from a text book however diligently studied.

Mount Moran carries no less than five glaciers. The three clinging to its north slopes are collectively called the Triple Glaciers. Skillet Glacier, so named because of its resemblance to a frying pan, is a conspicuous ice field in a shallow cirque on the east slope of the mountain, and is best seen from the village of Moran. Most interesting of all is Falling Ice Glacier, which lies high on the precipitous southeast face of Mount Moran. It has persisted on this the sunny side of the peak by reason of the cavernous cirque in which it lies entrenched and because it is shaded by two colossal rock towers, leaving its surface exposed to direct sunlight for only a part of each day. The trough down which the ice tongue extends is so steep that moraines cannot form, and the position of its terminus is determined not by melting but by the calving off of ice masses, which, in July and August, occasionally break away with thunderous reports. The stream from this glacier empties into Leigh Lake and gives to the water in its northwest corner the characteristic blue-green color due to suspended rock flour.

In the range there are also many small residual ice fields which are thought to be transitional between true glaciers and the fields of coarsely-crystalline snow termed névé. It would seem appropriate to call these "vestigial glaciers." Further examination will probably indicate that some of these retain sufficient glacial character to justify their being ranked as true glaciers.

In their decline, the great valley glaciers of the ice age shrank to disconnected remnants that persisted for a long time on the shaded north-facing slopes. In these situations glacial erosion continued after it had ceased in other parts of the range, and consequently such slopes now exhibit fresher glacial features than those found elsewhere. In ascending any deep canyon the mountaineer discovers that the north-facing walls are steeper than others, and, because incised by numerous cirques, much more complex in their sculpturing. Noteworthy, too, are the many perched lakes, such as Rimrock and Hanging lakes, that occupy north-facing cirques and gulches. As for the peaks, on those which still bear glaciers—Mount Moran, the Grand Teton, and the Middle Teton—the cutting back of the sheer north faces, with the resultant sharpening of the summits, still goes on apace, and on most others there is evidence pointing to the existence of similarly situated glaciers at a not remote time. Thus it has come about that the Teton peaks, without important exception, present their steepest and most spectacular faces toward the north. Witness the tremendous precipices on Mount Wister, Buck Mountain, and, greatest of all, the Grand Teton.

The contrast between sunny south exposures and shaded north ones is reflected also in the distribution of snow fields. In July or August, when it may appear that snow is all but gone in the mountains, one need only seek a more northerly point of vantage to bring into sight the large snow fields still clinging to almost every north slope.

Teton Clouds and Shadows

INTO THE TETON LANDSCAPE enter many elements which are ceaselessly changing, producing combinations that are new and beautiful. Even the contour of the range undergoes change, as we have observed, but in the large view this is imperceptible, so that seeking permanence in a universe of change we turn to mountains such as these for a symbol of everlastingness.

Over these seemingly changeless mountains, in endless succession, move the ephemeral colors of dawn and sunset and of noon and night, the shadows and the sunlight, the garlands of clouds with which storms adorn the peaks, the misty rain-curtains of afternoon showers. On the range are often set the rainbows; more rarely appears the alpenglow. Along the lower slopes appear the varying shades which the seasons bring to the aspen groves, and in the open meadows unnumbered flowers spring to life and beauty, each for its period and soon replaced by others, perhaps of equal brilliance but of different hues. High above are the snow fields, likewise changing and assuming new patterns as from spring to fall they dwindle, until at last all lose their identity in the mantle of breathless white silence that winter casts upon the region. We see the range now shining with snow, now darkly fearsome in storm, now serene and clean-washed after rain. Always it is changing, yet always it is beautiful.

Early and late in the day the sunlight falls aslant upon

the range, throwing its features into strong relief by high lights and shadows. Then it is that the tremendous depth of the chasms is most apparent, as are also the faceted character of the summits and the finer sculptural details everywhere graven in their faces. Then also the range is most awe-inspiring, and yet at the same time it has a mystical, entrancing beauty.

There is no jutting crag or promontory that does not at some hour catch the sun, and at others withdraw into shadow. The shadows are never harsh blacks. They assume pastel shades of blue and purple that run through every conceivable tone, each of which deepens when seen through an opening in the green forest, an optical phenomenon that almost everyone discovers for himself sooner or later.

The hours of early morning or late afternoon provide the best conditions for viewing the Tetons, and there is no better way of seeking a first acquaintance with them than to visit, at these hours, some point far enough distant to afford an unbroken panorama embracing the full sweep of the range, from Buck Mountain on the south to Eagles Rest and beyond on the north. Deadman's Bar, six miles out on the flats, is one such place often visited, and there are others with much in their favor. If time is very limited, a short stroll out into the sagebrush will suffice to open up a part of the view.

In the middle hours the illumination, being from above, is intense and searching, and falls with too nearly equal value on all the landscape to produce strong contrasts. The shadows on the mountain walls then pale or vanish, the lighting grows severe, and the range assumes an aspect of flatness all out of keeping with its actual rugged relief.

BREAKUP OF A STORM

THE TETON RANGE IN SUNSET PROFILE

TETON PEAKS GLIMPSED THROUGH THE CLOUDS

AFTER A SNOWSTORM IN THE TETONS

All this the artist knows full well. He also knows that the mirrorlike morning reflections on the lakes are not for the late riser, for as soon as air currents begin to move up the canyons ripples disturb the placid surface of the water. In some respects it is the artist who acquires the clearest understanding of the mountains, for he cannot successfully paint them without first having studied them attentively to learn their varying moods. He it is who is astir with the mountaineer before sunrise, and who a few hours later returns with a canvas that his critic may yawningly dismiss as "overdone" because, having never seen a mountain dawn, he cannot believe that such color effects exist. But whatever the artist's objective or schedule, his paintbox is usually put away from ten in the morning until three in the afternoon, the interval during which colors, shadows, clouds, and reflections are likely to be least impressive.

Late in the afternoon as the sun sinks behind the Teton Range a great shadow moves eastward across the floor of Jackson Hole. Probably few of the thousands who pass through the valley, or even those who spend their lives there, give thought to this daily phenomenon other than to note, perhaps, how the rampart range to the west shortens the length of day in the valley; yet in the perspective that one may gain from the Teton heights the afternoon shadow is a marvelous thing to see, reproducing as it does in silhouette the profile of the range. Unseen, this spectacle has been reënacted daily through the ages; even now few witness it because it takes place at an hour when most hikers and climbers are well on their homeward trek, and already have descended too low. Also, in its swift and soundless course across the valley it may pass unnoticed, for we can be unbelievably oblivious to Nature's offerings, failing to observe unusual cloud displays, celestial phenomena, and the aurora largely because we have the world too much with us even when in the wilderness. Some day the Teton shadow range will become celebrated, and then many will gladly climb the heights to see it, as now they seek them for the sunrise.

I first saw this spectacle in 1929 from near Ramshead Lake, after a late descent from Symmetry Spire. Chancing to glance downward, my attention was riveted by the scene on the valley floor. The shadow peaks of Rockchuck, St. John, and Symmetry Spire were already formed; and from a point a little lower and less obstructed those of Teewinot, the Grand Teton, and Nez Perce came into view (the shadows of Mount Owen and the South Teton merging with those of their forepeaks). At first low and blunt, the shadow peaks lengthened until each had attained its proper relative height, and the full profile was recognizable as that of the familiar Teton skyline. Only for a moment was this so; to have held this picture one would, like Joshua, have had to bid the sun stand still. With increasing distortion and accelerated speed as they were cast more and more obliquely, the shadow peaks pushed onward, crossed the Snake, and, grown to narrow, needle-sharp points, grotesque exaggerations even of peaks as slender as these, raced across the final stretch of Antelope Flats to the far edge of the sagebrush. The Grand Teton shadow was the first to reach it. With all the valley in shade, the peak shadows could still be seen mounting the wooded slopes beyond, but at last these, too, were all obscured, and the phantom range was gone.

Travel to the Tetons is largely confined to the summer

season, which at best is brief. In the spring, swift storms continue to whiten the peaks, along the base of which lie persistent snowdrifts that mark the avalanches of the past winter. But one by one the passes are opened, until, by June, from the four points of the compass visitors stream over the mountains into Jackson Hole. The busy weeks of summer which follow are few and fleeting and, while they last, filled with a beauty so enchanting that time passes unheeded and one is never prepared for the brooding gray days of late August. Then more frequent storms again bring fresh snow to the summits as a prelude to Indian summer, sunset of the year, when one hears in the distance the bugling of the elk, and on the mountainsides sees the aspens turn to gold.

A dweller of the city or lowlands, finding his way to the Tetons at any of these seasons, will discover that here earth and sky meet on terms of undreamed intimacy. Here summits rise aloft to form steps whereby he can literally no less than imaginatively ascend to the very clouds. And here clouds in their turn ofttimes descend to earth, there to renew association with glaciers and with lakes.

Impressive beyond any telling are those mornings when one awakens to find that in the night clouds have taken possession of the range. Daylight reveals them, poised over the cirques, wreathed about the peaks, or draped in festoons between them, settling into the canyons and trailing slowly along the mountain front. There are days when clouds sink even to the level of Jackson Hole, and with cool, moist fingers touch the tips of the firs, or come to rest over the still lakes. For all that may be seen now, the nearest mountains might be a thousand miles away. Sooner or later the gray curtain rises, and there come into view all up and down the

range the gleaming white cascades and waterfalls, each re-
vived and refreshed from the rain that has fallen above.

Many of the summer storms come in the afternoon. As I
have seen them year after year from camps on Jenny Lake,
these are brief and dramatic.

Though perhaps foretold several hours by clouds gather-
ing in the range, such a storm almost always breaks with
startling suddenness. An arresting sound comes from the
west shore, that of the wind bursting from the mouth of
Cascade Canyon and encountering the heavy forest. Simul-
taneously a white line appears on the lake, which advances
swiftly. By their agitation the trees on the shore also mark
the progress of the storm front. The sound of a gale in the
pines is always impressive, and at times alarming. It is sus-
tained like the held notes of cellos in an orchestra, but as
the storm approaches there is a crescendo such as no baton
ever summoned. Now it sounds in the trees overhead, all
about.

The lodgepole pines give proof of their marvelous elas-
ticity. It is remarkable that all are not snapped or uprooted,
considering the violence with which they sway and toss. An
occasional report does tell of a breaking stem, accounting
for broken snags and windfalls throughout the forest—the
toll of past storms.

The lake is rising, its surface flecked with white. The first
gusts tear the wave crests into sheets of spray. With good
reason rowers are cautioned to stay near shore when a storm
is imminent, for with wind coming from the canyon like
this a boat in the open might be caught in desperate plight.

Usually rain does not set in at once. One can stand by the
shore for several minutes as onlooker of the pageant in

which all Nature takes part. Gradually the agitation of trees
and waves becomes more subdued, and when the first big
drops strike the water the whitecaps may all have disappeared. From high in the range thunder speaks for the first
time, quickly the mountains vanish behind a veil of rain,
and the pines straighten, holding out their arms to the rain
which now descends in generous measure.

We had come to believe that the wind brought destruction
only to the trees that were poorly rooted or otherwise weak-
ened. Then on the stormy night of September 22, 1933,
came a blast from Cascade Canyon that swept across the
lake and through the forests beyond, felling almost every
tree within a quarter-mile strip across the moraine and
devastating much of the Jenny Lake campground. Thousands of trees were uprooted or broken, all thrown eastward
away from the canyon. Fortunately no one had remained
in the camp so late in the season. One large pine fell across
and demolished the tent which I, with my wife and little son,
had vacated not many days before. The wreckage of the
storm was eventually removed, but the forest clearings remain to record a weather caprice such as has occurred but
rarely, if one may judge from the continuity of the forests
elsewhere.

A summer of periodic rains is one of few forest fires and,
therefore, of freedom from worry on the part of the rangers
responsible for the protection of the forests. But occasionally come times of drouth that cause great anxiety, neces-
sitating ceaseless watchfulness and special fire patrols. Each
new cloudless day heightens the tension, and as week after
week the mountain slopes grow drier and the trails more
dusty the menace of fire becomes of grave concern to all.

At such times a thunderstorm may relieve the situation, at least locally, by bringing drenching showers; but if there is little rain the storm may paradoxically make the situation even more critical by leaving in its wake a scattering of fires set by lightning. These, however difficult to reach, must be extinguished at once. So effective is the protection afforded by the ranger staff that no fire within the park has yet gotten out of control, or even assumed serious proportions.

Snow is possible in any month. As a rule the cloud formations that bring it are larger and more formless than others, and linger over the range in a curiously caressing manner.

The snow of summer or early fall comes with a delicate beauty of its own. Perhaps the peaks have long been nearly bare, when one night rain comes to the valley. Because they are mantled with clouds, one knows not the fate of the peaks until at sunrise the mists begin to disperse. Then here and there through cloud rifts are revealed the summits; and behold, they are covered with new snow. It lies on ledges and along the couloirs, emphasizing unsuspected lines in the faces of the most familiar peaks. So white is it that by comparison the shining clouds seem gray. The revelation is brief, for the sun of the new day drives away the clouds, and with them the snow also takes flight. But the scene is imperishably engraved in memory.

Clouds—creatures of sky, to be sure; yet they are thoroughly at home here among the mountains, enjoying close fellowship with peaks and canyons. Large is their contribution to the landscape, adding life and movement to scenes otherwise in eternal repose. When they are absent, the moun-

tains seem austere and bare, and in periods of prolonged
drouth one feels vague uneasiness and expectancy. On their
return, how unfailing is one's response to their beauty, how
eagerly all their movements and changes of form are again
followed.

So, for the Teton visitor, clouds and their ways become
subjects of absorbing interest.

In the lowlands clouds seem more remote than in reality
they are, there being no means of estimating their height.
But in the Tetons the range serves as a scale, conveniently
graduated as it is with lakes, glaciers, and summits of known
elevation.

It is a July day and, high above, a thousand silvery cu-
muli are silently afloat, casting blue shadows on the slopes
and valleys below. As they drift slowly along they clear the
highest of the peaks, evidence enough that they must be
well over 7,500 feet above our station on the valley floor.
But on another day such clouds, possibly larger and darker,
less regular of form, are sufficiently low to graze the Grand
Teton. They are, then, about 7,000 feet above us and nearly
14,000 feet above the level of the sea. Eventually, as they
mass more heavily, they obscure the Three Tetons and
Mount Owen, just touching the summit pinnacle of Teewinot. Now they are about 1,500 feet lower than when first
observed.

The range not only intercepts the passing clouds; it actually gives birth to many. These are the most fascinating
of all. Their forms are legion, and many of their ways devi-
ous past finding out, yet one can, with observation, learn
much concerning their place and manner of formation.

One type seems fairly obvious. The glaciers and snow

fields chill the overlying air so that at times its moisture condenses. On frosty mornings little cloud caps so formed may often be seen, for instance, over Falling Ice Glacier and the east-face snow fields of Teewinot, this despite the general absence of clouds elsewhere. Such clouds are ordinarily short-lived, but if the air is still they may persist for hours.

Other clouds are probably produced by the air currents that encounter the range. Forced sharply upward, these expand and cool. Condensation may occur at various altitudes, depending upon the prevailing conditions of temperature and humidity. When it takes place at low elevations, great cloud banks roll up along the range, and at times blot it from view; when higher, more scattered clouds form here and there among the peaks. As the currents flow along lines predetermined by the contours of the range, they tend to produce clouds at points where they must rise over divides and peaks. Some clouds are best explained in terms of convection, or by the mixing of air from currents of different humidity and temperature.

It is not uncommon to find clouds forming at the very mountaintops. These may linger where formed, may drift some distance away before vanishing, or may be launched in a train miles long, reaching clear across and beyond Jackson Hole.

Teewinot, it has seemed to me, produces the most varied and unusual of clouds. Of many memorable displays, I recall one with special vividness. Late one August afternoon it alone of all the peaks in sight started to form a summit cloud, a solitary formation that grew with extraordinary rapidity, both outward and upward, until in less than half an hour it had become a towering edifice with rounded, glistening white contours, wonderfully smooth and substantial looking. A structure so grandiose could not stand long, and, as I watched, it sank about the summit into shapeless ruins. There was still no other cloud in the range.

Very different was the situation on another August day, suggested in the following note made at the time: "A scene today such as I have not previously observed. At noon when I passed Timbered Island a little cloud cap was hanging over each of the major peaks all the way from Buck Mountain to Eagles Rest. East of the valley were two more, over Jackson Peak and Sheep Mountain. But they were all increasing in size, and an hour or two later, when I again passed this way, nearly all had merged."

Such scenes cannot lose their interest though watched year after year, and references to them crowd my summer journals. To quote a few from one month:

"July 4. Awoke to an overcast sky. Air cool and misty. For several hours this morning the thunder rumbled solemnly over the range (without, however, any distinct peals) as though the peaks were conversing. If peaks could speak, such, I fancy, would be their voices."

"July 11. Storms and sunshine have alternated about the high peaks both yesterday and today with a swiftness almost bewildering."

"July 21. All day clouds have been streaming about among the crags of the near-by peaks, especially St. John, and our handful of visitors have been watching them from the ranger cabin. They have said little, and spoken only in hushed tones of the changing scenes up above, feeling well repaid, I am sure, for the rain and muddy roads they braved to get here. At evening the clouds miraculously dissolved and the summits emerged, fresh and radiant in the sunset."

As was true on that particular July evening, during the hour of sunset the range almost always joins with the heavens in declaring the glory of God, and frequently it happens that of the two the mountains show forth the greater splendor.

For at this time the lofty, richly sculptured north walls of the ridges and peaks one by one emerge from their shadows, even as the other slopes sink into obscurity. Receiving full on their faces the light from the northwest, they take fire, till every crag and pinnacle shines with the brilliance of burnished gold. When the sun passes beneath the horizon this direct illumination is cut off, and now the great precipices assume various colors, crimson, lavender, or rose, whose tones and intensities vary with those in the evening sky from which they are reflected. Slowly, reluctantly, these colors fade from the mountains as they fade from the heavens, but they linger long into the dusk on the very summits of Nez Perce, Teewinot, and others of the high peaks.

Late in the evening, should one stroll down to the lake for a final view of the range, the peak faces might be found still touched with a pale light, as if giving back the last of the radiance received at sunset. But this light, unlike that of a few hours earlier, is silvery and unfading, for it is a light that is shed from the stars. Through the long hours of night it continues, unless extinguished by clouds or, at moonrise, merged in a sudden greater brightness.

Moonlight in its fullest flood brings a spectacle of beauty causing one to abandon every thought of rest, and, heedless of the hour, to set forth anew, as though it were the dawn of day and not its close. For again the features of the range are lighted, but gone now is every trace of austerity, the severeness that by day may frighten or appall. This nocturnal outpouring of light, as revealing almost as day, is infinitely soft and tender, and is deeply fraught with mystery.

No denying fancy now its sway. Are not the peaks grown taller, of nobler stature even than before? Motionless, yet they are alive, these spectral figures, this night met in voiceless conclave for deliberations man may neither share nor comprehend. No matter; enough to be abroad at such a time. And as one starts forth in the night it is with bated breath and cautious step, lest any sound escape and break the reverent silence.

Index